THE
ANTHOLOGY
ANTHOLOGY

THE ANTHOLOGY ANTHOLOGY

A selection from 30 years of CBC Radio's "Anthology"

EDITED BY

Robert Weaver

FOREWORD BY

Alice Munro

Macmillan of Canada
A Division of Gage Publishing Limited
Toronto Canada

CBC Enterprises/Les Entreprises Radio-Canada
Montreal   Toronto   New York   London

Canadian Cataloguing in Publication Data

Main entry under title:
The Anthology anthology

ISBN 0-7715-9822-X

1. Canadian fiction (English)—20th century.* 2. Canadian poetry (English)—20th century.* I. Weaver, Robert, date. II. Anthology (Radio program)

PS8233.A58 1984   C810′.8′0054   C84-099261-0
PR9194.9.A58 1984

Design by John Murtagh
Printed in Canada

Macmillan of Canada
A Division of Gage Publishing Limited
Toronto, Canada

In memory of Nathan Cohen

CONTENTS

FOREWORD

BY ALICE MUNRO

In the spring of 1951 I sold Robert Weaver a story for the program *Canadian Short Stories*. Our correspondence began then, and I met him for the first time in the fall of 1953. For the next dozen or so years he was almost the only person I knew who had anything to do with the world of writing. He was one of the two—or possibly three—people who took my writing seriously. I would send him stories. He would buy them, or send them back. If he sent them back, there would always be a long letter telling me why. He never passed out judgements as anything final. He left me lots of room for disagreement, and was always ready to look at a story again, with changes I had made according to his criticisms or sometimes quite against them. Sometimes he would reconsider a story in which no changes had been made, and occasionally reverse an opinion, finding some power or grace in it he hadn't been able to see before.

He also wrote me letters when I hadn't sent him anything, when I hadn't written anything, and it was these letters, especially, that gave me nourishment and hope. I had very barren times. Most young writers do. (Older writers do, too, and he wasn't forgetting about them.) These bad times come whether the writers are isolated, as I was, or buffeted by lively competition; whether they are young English teachers sweating under the weight of all that's been written already, or young cab-drivers longing to kick all that in the teeth, or young housewives and mothers who feel their wits going soggy in the wash-water.

His letters didn't promise anything in particular. They didn't reprove me for not writing or exhort me to get busy. They reminded me that I was a writer. The most precious encouragement was not in what they said, but in what they took for granted.

He never gave up. His faith sometimes made me fretful, as can happen when somebody knows something about you better than you know it yourself. More often it gave me energy, and a renewed sense of possibilities I had almost lost sight of.

I wasn't the only one. All over the country, unknown writers, and writers beginning to be known, and writers who hadn't written anything for a while, were getting these letters. They were being prodded into writing when they thought they had no time to write, when they were sick of sending things off to impossible markets and unresponsive editors, when their ideas of what and why they wanted to write seemed to be getting muddied and mislaid. He was keeping us going, not making any rash promises, getting the best he could out of us, not coddling, but giving us what we needed most—his serious attention, his reasonable hopes, a real market.

He took something else for granted—that it was possible to have in Canada a market, an audience, for Canadian writing. This was long before such a view became fashionable. I remember, in the late fifties, a man whose opinions I respected saying to me that he "made a point of never reading a Canadian book". This was a somewhat extreme position, but not unacceptable at that time for Canadians who wished to be thought discriminating.

Ten, twenty years later, such boasts would not be heard. Robert Weaver must be given a good deal of the credit for that. He did all this for Canadian writing without ever putting on nationalistic blinkers. And his attention goes on and on. He was in touch with the generation before mine, and he knows just as well the writers who are the age of my children. He never limited his interest to one kind of writing, to any particular kind of material or set of preoccupations. He understands the breadth and diversity we need to have a literature.

I hope this will give some idea of the contribution of a man who will never make such claims for himself.

July 1984

PREFACE

The first broadcast of *Anthology*, a CBC literary program, on October 19, 1954, included a group of poems by Norman Levine and a short story, "The Secret of the Kugel", by Mordecai Richler. Both were young, relatively unknown writers at the time; both are still writing and their work is well known not only in Canada but in a number of countries abroad. I'm sure that no one connected with that first broadcast of *Anthology* imagined that the program would have so much staying power, the CBC such patience, or that a radio series would play some part in the development of modern Canadian writing. But it happened that way, and so, for *Anthology*'s thirtieth anniversary, here is a sampling from the program's archives.

When I went to work for the CBC on November 1, 1948, one of the programs I was given to organize was a fifteen-minute short-story series called *Canadian Short Stories*. In the next few years, frustrated by the program's length, we sometimes found time on the network to broadcast a few longer stories. Narrative poems by such writers as Dorothy Livesay, Anne Marriott, Earle Birney, and E. J. Pratt were also being heard on CBC radio, sometimes as school broadcasts. We scheduled readings of poetry by modern English and American writers: D. H. Lawrence, T. S. Eliot, W. H. Auden, W. B. Yeats, Kenneth Patchen, William Carlos Williams are some of the names I remember from that time. Short stories by Canadian writers were read every afternoon on the CBC first in the series *Bernie Braden Tells a Story* and later on *Stories with John Drainie*. In the late 1940s and early 1950s there was quite a lot of literary programming on CBC radio, but its scheduling was less consistent than some of us would have liked.

So we invented *Anthology*, and the CBC was persuaded to schedule the program. It began as a weekly thirty-minute series with a modest budget. It has always been scheduled on the CBC's AM radio network, which means that it has been heard in cities, towns, and villages across the country from Newfoundland to Vancouver Island. Its fifty thousand listeners, a relatively small audience in radio terms, still make it by far the largest of Canadian "little magazines". In the fall of 1969, *Anthology* found its permanent home on Saturday night and became just under an hour in length. It includes poetry and short story readings, talks, interviews and discussions, features and documentaries. From time to time we have broadcast programs about movies and the theatre. Most of the material broadcast on *Anthology* has been by Canadian writers and performers, but we have tried not to ignore the rest of the world even during that period when cultural nationalism was fashionable in this country. We have had the good fortune to be able to broadcast many readings and literary features from the BBC.

Most magazines accept only unpublished material, stories and poems, articles and reviews that are appearing in print for the first time. On *Anthology* we've broadcast unpublished poems and stories but also literary works that had already appeared in magazines or books. We wanted our listeners to be able to hear a wide variety of the fiction and poetry that was being written in Canada at any given time. However, for this book we've limited ourselves to poems and stories and memoirs and interviews that actually received their first publication on the program. Even so, many writers and some genres unfortunately could not be represented here. Literary features and documentaries designed for radio broadcast do not in most cases translate well to print. Works-in-progress, which have often been a feature on *Anthology*, such as the excerpts we broadcast from Mordecai Richler's great novels, *The Apprenticeship of Duddy Kravitz*, *St. Urbain's Horseman*, and *Joshua Then and Now*, have since become available in the complete works, of which we were proud to be able to offer a preview.

Many writers and performers and CBC producers have contributed to *Anthology* since 1954, and I want to thank all of them here. Much of the credit for the program's beginnings belongs to Robert Harlow, then a CBC producer in Vancouver, who later left the Corporation to write novels and to teach in the department of creative writing at the University of British Columbia.

In 1980 Sean Berrigan prepared a catalogue and an index of *Anthology* from 1954 to 1974—a formidable task, considering the state of our records—in part fulfilment of a Master of Arts degree at Carleton University in Ottawa. Mr. Berrigan's work has been invaluable for us in many ways.

For help in the preparation of this book I want to thank Eithne Black, Katherine Carolan, Faye Macpherson, Howard Engel, Eric Friesen, and Keith Gill of the CBC; also, CBC Program Archives and CBC Enterprises; and at Macmillan of Canada, Anne Holloway and Doug Gibson.

Robert Weaver
July 1984

ALICE MUNRO

"The Shining Houses" is an early Alice Munro story that was published in her first collection, Dance of the Happy Shades *(McGraw-Hill Ryerson, 1968), for which she won her first Governor General's Award.* Dance of the Happy Shades *was a book that required fifteen years of dedication and determination from a young writer who was largely unknown. During that time she published in* Chatelaine, *on* Anthology, *and in three small magazines,* The Montrealer, The Canadian Forum, *and* The Tamarack Review. *Traditionally, this was how young writers were expected to launch their careers. Now, when Alice Munro has a glowing reputation in Canada and abroad, it is a great pleasure to see that in her case the traditional method did work. Her most recent book is* The Moons of Jupiter *(Macmillan, 1982).*

❀

The Shining Houses

Mary sat on the back steps of Mrs. Fullerton's house, talking—or really listening—to Mrs. Fullerton, who sold her eggs. She had come in to pay the egg money, on her way to Edith's Debbie's birthday party. Mrs. Fullerton did not pay calls herself and she did not invite them, but, once a business pretext was established, she liked to talk. And Mary found herself exploring her neighbour's life as she had once explored the lives of grandmothers and aunts—by pretending to know less than she did, asking for some story she had heard before; this way, remembered episodes emerged each time with slight differences of content, meaning, colour, yet with a pure reality that usually attaches to things which are at least part legend. She had almost forgotten that there are people whose lives can be seen like this. She did not talk to many old people any more. Most of the people she knew had lives like her own, in which things were not sorted out yet, and it is not certain if this thing, or that, should be taken seriously. Mrs. Fullerton had no doubts or ques-

1

tions of this kind. How was it possible, for instance, not to take seriously the broad blithe back of Mr. Fullerton, disappearing down the road on a summer day, not to return?

"I didn't know that," said Mary. "I always thought Mr. Fullerton was dead."

"He's no more dead than I am," said Mrs. Fullerton, sitting up straight. A bold Plymouth Rock walked across the bottom step and Mary's little boy, Danny, got up to give rather cautious chase. "He's just gone off on his travels, that's what he is. May of gone up north, may of gone to the States, I don't know. But he's not dead. I would of felt it. He's not old neither, you know, not old like I am. He was my second husband, he was younger. I never made any secret of it. I had this place and raised my children and buried my first husband, before ever Mr. Fullerton came upon the scene. Why, one time down in the post office we was standing together by the wicket and I went over to put a letter in the box and left my bag behind me, and Mr. Fullerton turns to go after me and the girl calls to him, she says, here, your mother's left her purse!"

Mary smiled, answering Mrs. Fullerton's high-pitched and not trustful laughter. Mrs. Fullerton was old, as she had said—older than you might think, seeing her hair still fuzzy and black, her clothes slatternly-gay, dime-store brooches pinned to her ravelling sweater. Her eyes showed it, black as plums, with a soft inanimate sheen; things sank into them and they never changed. The life in her face was all in the nose and mouth, which were always twitching, fluttering, drawing tight grimace-lines down her cheeks. When she came around every Friday on her egg deliveries her hair was curled, her blouse held together by a bunch of cotton flowers, her mouth painted, a spidery and ferocious line of red; she would not show herself to her new neighbours in any sad old-womanish disarray.

"Thought I was his mother," she said. "I didn't care. I had a good laugh. But what I was telling you," she said, "a day in summer, he was off work. He had the ladder up and he was picking me the cherries off of my black-cherry tree. I came out to hang my clothes and there was this man I never seen before in my life, taking the pail of cherries my husband hands down to him. Helping himself, too, not backward, he sat down and ate cherries out of my pail. Who's that, I said to my husband, and he says, just a fellow passing. If he's a friend of yours, I said, he's welcome to stay for supper. What are you talking about, he says, I never seen him before. So I never said another thing. Mr. Fullerton went and talked to him, eating my cherries I intended for a pie, but that man would talk to anybody, tramp, Jehovah's Witness, anybody—that didn't need to mean anything.

"And half an hour after that fellow went off," she said, "Mr. Fullerton comes out in his brown jacket and his hat on. I have to meet a man downtown. How long will you be, I said. Oh, not long. So off he goes down the road, walking down to where the old tram went—we was all in the bush then—and something made me look after him. He must be hot in that coat, I said. And that's when I knew he wasn't coming back. Yet I couldn't've expected it, he liked it here. He was talking about putting chinchillas in the back yard. What's in a man's mind even when you're living with him you will never know."

"Was it long ago?" said Mary.

"Twelve years. My boys wanted me to sell then and go and live in rooms. But I said no. I had my hens and a nanny goat too at that time. More or less a pet. I had a pet coon too for a while, used to feed him chewing gum. Well, I said, husbands maybe come and go, but a place you've lived fifty years is something else. Making a joke of it with my family. Besides, I thought, if Mr. Fullerton was to come back, he'd come back here, not knowing where else to go. Of course he'd hardly know where to find me, the way it's changed now. But I always had the idea he might of suffered a loss of memory and it might come back. That has happened.

"I'm not complaining. Sometimes it seems to me about as reasonable a man should go as stay. I don't mind changes, either, that helps out my egg business. But this baby-sitting. All the time one or the other is asking me about baby-sitting. I tell them I got my own house to sit in and I raised my share of children."

Mary, remembering the birthday party, got up and called to her little boy. "I thought I might offer my black cherries for sale next summer," Mrs. Fullerton said. "Come and pick your own and they're fifty cents a box. I can't risk my old bones up a ladder no more."

"That's too much," Mary said, smiling. "They're cheaper than that at the supermarket." Mrs. Fullerton already hated the supermarket for lowering the price of eggs. Mary shook out her last cigarette and left it with her, saying she had another package in her purse. Mrs. Fullerton was fond of a cigarette but would not accept one unless you took her by surprise. Baby-sitting would pay for them, Mary thought. At the same time she was rather pleased with Mrs. Fullerton for being so unaccommodating. When Mary came out of this place, she always felt as if she were passing through barricades. The house and its surroundings were so self-sufficient,

with their complicated and seemingly unalterable layout of vegetables and flower beds, apple and cherry trees, wired chicken-run,
berry patch and wooden walks, woodpile, a great many roughly
built dark little sheds, for hens or rabbits or a goat. Here was no
open or straightforward plan, no order that an outsider could
understand; yet what was haphazard time had made final. The
place had become fixed, impregnable, all its accumulations necessary, until it seemed that even the wash-tubs, mops, couch springs
and stacks of old police magazines on the back porch were there to
stay.

Mary and Danny walked down the road that had been called, in
Mrs. Fullerton's time, Wicks Road, but was now marked on the
maps of the subdivision as Heather Drive. The name of the
subdivision was Garden Place, and its streets were named for
flowers. On either side of the road the earth was raw; the ditches
were running full. Planks were laid across the open ditches, planks
approached the doors of the newest houses. The new, white and
shining houses, set side by side in long rows in the wound of the
earth. She always thought of them as white houses, though of
course they were not entirely white. They were stucco and siding,
and only the stucco was white; the siding was painted in shades of
blue, pink, green and yellow, all fresh and vivid colours. Last year,
just at this time, in March, the bulldozers had come in to clear away
the brush and second-growth and great trees of the mountain
forest; in a little while the houses were going up among the
boulders, the huge torn stumps, the unimaginable upheavals of that
earth. The houses were frail at first, skeletons of new wood
standing up in the dusk of the cold spring days. But the roofs went
on, black and green, blue and red, and the stucco, the siding; the
windows were put in, and plastered with signs that said, Murry's
Glass, French's Hardwood Floors; it could be seen that the houses
were real. People who would live in them came out and tramped
around in the mud on Sundays. They were for people like Mary and
her husband and their child, with not much money but expecta-
tions of more; Garden Place was already put down, in the minds of
people who understood addresses, as less luxurious than Pine Hills
but more desirable than Wellington Park. The bathrooms were
beautiful, with three-part mirrors, ceramic tile, and coloured
plumbing. The cupboards in the kitchen were light birch or
mahogany, and there were copper lighting fixtures there and in the
dining ells. Brick planters, matching the fireplaces, separated the
living rooms and halls. The rooms were all large and light and the
basements dry, and all this soundness and excellence seemed to be

clearly, proudly indicated on the face of each house—those ingenuously similar houses that looked calmly out at each other, all the way down the street.

Today, since it was Saturday, all the men were out working around their houses. They were digging drainage ditches and making rockeries and clearing off and burning torn branches and brush. They worked with competitive violence and energy, all this being new to them; they were not men who made their livings by physical work. All day Saturday and Sunday they worked like this, so that in a year or two there should be green terraces, rock walls, shapely flower beds and ornamental shrubs. The earth must be heavy to dig now; it had been raining last night and this morning. But the day was brightening; the clouds had broken, revealing a long thin triangle of sky, its blue still cold and delicate, a winter colour. Behind the houses on one side of the road were pine trees, their ponderous symmetry not much stirred by any wind. These were to be cut down any day now, to make room for a shopping centre, which had been promised when the houses were sold.

And under the structure of this new subdivision, there was still something else to be seen; that was the old city, the old wilderness city that had lain on the side of the mountain. It had to be called a city because there were tramlines running into the woods, the houses had numbers and there were all the public buildings of a city, down by the water. But houses like Mrs. Fullerton's had been separated from each other by uncut forest and a jungle of wild blackberry and salmonberry bushes; these surviving houses, with thick smoke coming out of their chimneys, walls unpainted and patched and showing different degrees of age and darkening, rough sheds and stacked wood and compost heaps and grey board fences around them—these appeared every so often among the large new houses of Mimosa and Marigold and Heather Drive—dark, enclosed, expressing something like savagery in their disorder and the steep, unmatched angles of roofs and lean-tos; not possible on these streets, but there.

"What are they saying," said Edith, putting on more coffee. She was surrounded in her kitchen by the ruins of the birthday party—cake and moulded jellies and cookies with animal faces. A balloon rolled underfoot. The children had been fed, had posed for flash cameras and endured the birthday games; now they were playing in the back bedrooms and the basement, while their parents had coffee. "What are they saying in there?" said Edith.

"I wasn't listening," Mary said, holding the empty cream pitcher in her hand. She went to the sink window. The rent in the clouds had been torn wide open and the sun was shining. The house seemed too hot.

"Mrs. Fullerton's house," said Edith, hurrying back to the living-room. Mary knew what they were talking about. Her neighbours' conversation, otherwise not troubling, might at any moment snag itself on this subject and eddy menacingly in familiar circles of complaint, causing her to look despairingly out of windows, or down into her lap, trying to find some wonderful explanatory word to bring it to a stop; she did not succeed. She had to go back; they were waiting for cream.

A dozen neighbourhood women sat around the living room, absently holding the balloons they had been given by their children. Because the children on the street were so young, and also because any gathering-together of the people who lived there was considered a healthy thing in itself, most birthday parties were attended by mothers as well as children. Women who saw each other every day met now in earrings, nylons and skirts, with their hair fixed and faces applied. Some of the men were there too—Steve, who was Edith's husband, and others he had invited in for beer; they were all in their work clothes. The subject just introduced was one of the few on which male and female interest came together.

"I tell you what I'd do if I was next door to it," Steve said, beaming good-naturedly in expectation of laughter. "I'd send my kids over there to play with matches."

"Oh, funny," Edith said. "It's past joking. You joke, I try to do something. I even phoned the Municipal Hall."

"What did they say?" said Mary Lou Ross.

"Well *I* said couldn't they get her to paint it, at least, or pull down some of the shacks, and they said no they couldn't. I said I thought there must be some kind of ordinance applied to people like that and they said they knew how I *felt* and they were very sorry—"

"But no?"

"But no."

"But what about the chickens, I thought—"

"Oh, they wouldn't let you or me keep chickens, but she has some special dispensation about that too, I forgot how it goes."

"I'm going to stop buying them," Janie Inger said. "The supermarket's cheaper and who cares that much about fresh? And my God, the smell. I said to Carl I knew we were coming to the sticks but I somehow didn't picture us next door to a barnyard."

"Across the street is worse than next door. It makes me wonder why we ever bothered with a picture window, whenever anybody comes to see us I want to draw the drapes so they won't see what's across from us."

"Okay, okay," Steve said, cutting heavily through these female voices. "What Carl and I started out to tell you was that, if we can work this lane deal, she has got to go. It's simple and it's legal. That's the beauty of it."

"What lane deal?"

"We are getting to that. Carl and I been cooking this for a couple of weeks, but we didn't like to say anything in case it didn't work out. Take it, Carl."

"Well she's on the lane allowance, that's all," Carl said. He was a real estate salesman, stocky, earnest, successful. "I had an idea it might be that way, so I went down to the Municipal Hall and looked it up."

"What does that mean, dear?" said Janie, casual, wifely.

"This is it," Carl said. "There's an allowance for a lane, there always has been, the idea being if the area ever got built up they would put a lane through. But they never thought that would happen, people just built where they liked. She's got part of her house and half a dozen shacks sitting right where the lane has to go through. So what we do now, we get the municipality to put through a lane. We need a lane anyway. Then she has to get out. It's the law."

"It's the law," said Steve, radiating admiration. "What a smart boy. These real estate operators are smart boys."

"Does she get anything?" said Mary Lou. "I'm sick of looking at it and all but I don't want to see anybody in the poorhouse."

"Oh, she'll get paid. More than it's worth. Look, it's to her advantage. She'll get paid for it, and she couldn't sell it, she couldn't give it away."

Mary set her coffee cup down before she spoke and hoped her voice would sound all right, not emotional or scared. "But remember she's been here a long time," she said. "She was here before most of us were born." She was trying desperately to think of other words, words more sound and reasonable than these; she could not expose to this positive tide any notion that they might think flimsy and romantic, or she would destroy her argument. But she had no argument. She could try all night and never find any words to stand up to their words, which came at her now invincibly from all sides: *shack, eyesore, filthy, property, value*.

"Do you honestly think that people who let their property get so

7

rundown have that much claim to our consideration?" Janie said, feeling her husband's plan was being attacked.

"She's been here forty years, now we're here," Carl said. "So it goes. And whether you realize it or not, just standing there that house is bringing down the resale value of every house on this street. I'm in the business, I know."

And these were joined by other voices; it did not matter much what they said as long as they were full of self-assertion and anger. That was their strength, proof of their adulthood, of themselves and their seriousness. The spirit of anger rose among them, bearing up their young voices, sweeping them together as on a flood of intoxication, and they admired each other in this new behaviour as property-owners as people admire each other for being drunk.

"We might as well get everybody now," Steve said. "Save going around to so many places."

It was supper time, getting dark out. Everybody was preparing to go home, mothers buttoning their children's coats, children clutching, without much delight, their balloons and whistles and paper baskets full of jelly beans. They had stopped fighting, almost stopped noticing each other; the party had disintegrated. The adults too had grown calmer and felt tired.

"Edith! Edith, have you got a pen?"

Edith brought a pen and they spread the petition for the lane, which Carl had drawn up, on the dining-room table, clearing away the paper plates with smears of dried ice cream. People began to sign mechanically as they said goodbye. Steve was still scowling slightly; Carl stood with one hand on the paper, businesslike, but proud. Mary knelt on the floor and struggled with Danny's zipper. She got up and put on her own coat, smoothed her hair, put on her gloves and took them off again. When she could not think of anything else to do she walked past the dining-room table on her way to the door. Carl held out the pen.

"I can't sign that," she said. Her face flushed up, at once, her voice was trembling. Steve touched her shoulder.

"What's the matter, honey?"

"I don't think we have the right. We haven't the right."

"Mary, don't you care how things look? You live here too."

"No, I—I don't care." Oh, wasn't it strange, how in your imagination, when you stood up for something, your voice rang, people started, abashed; but in real life they all smiled in rather a special way and you saw that what you had really done was serve yourself up as a conversational delight for the next coffee party.

"Don't worry, Mary, she's got money in the bank," Janie said. "She must have. I asked her to baby-sit for me once and she practically spit in my face. She isn't exactly a charming old lady, you know."

"I know she isn't a charming old lady," Mary said.

Steve's hand still rested on her shoulder. "Hey what do you think we are, a bunch of ogres?"

"Nobody wants to turn her out just for the fun of it," Carl said. "It's unfortunate. We all know that. But we have to think of the community."

"Yes," said Mary. But she put her hands in the pockets of her coat and turned to say thank you to Edith, thank you for the birthday party. It occurred to her that they were right, for themselves, for whatever it was they had to be. And Mrs. Fullerton was old, she had dead eyes, nothing could touch her. Mary went out and walked with Danny up the street. She saw the curtains being drawn across living-room windows; cascades of flowers, of leaves, of geometrical designs, shut off these rooms from the night. Outside it was quite dark, the white houses were growing dim, the clouds breaking and breaking, and smoke blowing from Mrs. Fullerton's chimney. The pattern of Garden Place, so assertive in the daytime, seemed to shrink at night into the raw black mountainside.

The voices in the living-room have blown away, Mary thought. If they would blow away and their plans be forgotten, if one thing could be left alone. But these are people who win, and they are good people; they want homes for their children, they help each other when there is trouble, they plan a community—saying that word as if they found a modern and well-proportioned magic in it, and no possibility anywhere of a mistake.

There is nothing you can do at present but put your hands in your pockets and keep a disaffected heart.

AL PURDY

Al Purdy lives in the village of Ameliasburg, near Belleville, Ontario, and much of what he has written—the poetry, and recently the beginnings of his memoirs—has been about this old Loyalist section of Eastern Ontario. But Purdy has also become a restless traveller, composing poems on Baffin Island (for North of Summer, 1967), in Cuba, Mexico, and South Africa, in Spain and Greece, and in many other countries.

Poems from all these places have been broadcast on Anthology, usually read by Purdy himself. Among our favourites has been a handful of poems written in the Galapagos Islands and broadcast during the 1970s. The poems included here have also been published in Al Purdy's Being Alive (McClelland & Stewart, 1978).

❖

Birdwatching at the Equator

The blue-footed booby
stands on her tropic island
in the Galapagos group
stands all day long
shading her eggs from the sun
also protecting her blue feet
from too much ultraviolet
Sometimes the male booby
flaps his wings and dances
to entertain his mate
pointing his toes upward
so they can discuss blueness
which seems to them very beautiful
Their only real enemy
is the piratical frigate bird
floating on great black wings
above the mile-long island
Sometimes the frigate bird

robs them of their fish
whereupon the booby
is wont to say "Friggit"
and catches some more
When night comes all the boobies
sit down at once as if
God had given them a signal
or else one booby says
to the rest "Let's flop boys"
and they do
The blue booby's own capsule
comment about evolution:
if God won't do it for you
do it yourself:
stand up
sit down
make love
have some babies
catch fish
dance sometimes
admire your feet
friggit:
what else is there?

Moonspell

I have forgotten English
in order to talk to pelicans
plunging into tomorrow
disturb the deep reverie
of herons standing
on yesterday's shoreline
find the iguana's secret
name embroidered
on his ruby brain

It is milk
it is moonlight
milk pouring
over the islands
stand in a doorway
listen
I am drowning
in sky milk
and those soft murmurings
of moonlit vertebrae
these deciphered codewords
are spoken names
of island dwellers
they will not be repeated
pour on my bare shoulders
are small extensions
of themselves
as the manta ray bubbles
rising in water
gleams in moonlight
small fish tremble
I know I know
my speech is grunts
squeaks clicks stammers
let go let go
follow the sunken ships
and deep sea creatures
follow the *protozoa*
into that far darkness
another kind of light
leave off this flesh
this voice these bones
sink down

NORMAN LEVINE

On the acknowledgements page of Thin Ice, *a collection of his stories published in 1979, Norman Levine mentions that eleven of the twelve stories in the book were broadcast on* Anthology, *and that eight of the stories were commissioned for the program. "We All Begin in a Little Magazine", which was first broadcast in 1971, has the distinction of being the first story by Norman Levine commissioned for* Anthology. *The story will also appear in the summer of 1984 in* Champagne Barn, *a retrospective collection of twenty-three stories by Norman Levine published by Penguin Books. Mr. Levine was born in Ottawa, he lived for many years in St. Ives, Cornwall, and he now lives in Toronto.*

❖

We All Begin in a Little Magazine

We live in a small coastal town. And in the summer, when the place is looking its best, it becomes overcrowded with people who have come away from the cities for their annual holiday by the sea. It is then that we leave and go up to London for our holiday.

My wife usually finds a house by looking through *The Times*. In this way we had the house of a man who built hotels in the poor parts of Africa so that wealthy American Negroes could go back to see where their grandparents came from. Another summer it was an architect's house where just about everything was done by push-button control. A third time, it was in a house whose owner was in the middle of getting a divorce—for non-consummation—and wanted to be out of the country.

This June she saw an ad saying: DOCTOR'S HOUSE AVAILABLE IN LONDON FOR THREE WEEKS. REASONABLE RENT. She phoned the number. And we agreed to take it.

The advertised house was central, near South Kensington tube station, not far from the Gardens. The taxi took us from Paddington—how pale people looked in London on a hot summer's day—

13

and brought us to a wide street, stopping in front of a detached all-white house with acacia trees in the front garden. A bottle of warm milk was on the doorstep. I opened the door with the key and brought our cases inside.

The phone was ringing.

"Hello," I said.

"Is this *ABC*?" a youthful voice asked.

"I'm sorry," I said. "You have the wrong number."

"What is your number?"

"Knightsbridge 4231," I said.

"That *is* the number," the voice said.

"There must be some mistake," I said. "This is a doctor's house."

"Is the doctor there?"

"No," I said. "He's on holiday."

"Can I leave a message for him?"

"Are you ill?"

"No," he said. "Tell him that David White rang. David White of Somerset. He has had my manuscript for over six months now. He said he would let me know over a month ago. I have written him four times."

"I'll tell him," I said.

"If he needs more time," the young man said hesitantly, "I don't mind—"

"OK," I said and hung up.

"I don't know what's going on here," I said to my wife.

But she and the children were busy exploring the rest of the house.

It was a large house and it looked as if it had been lived in. The front room was a children's room with all sorts of games and blackboards and toys and children's books and posters on the walls. There was the sitting-room, the bottom half of the walls were filled with books in shelves. There were more books in the hallway, on the sides of the stairs, and in shelves on every landing. There were three separate baths. A breakfast room where a friendly black cat slept most of the time on top of the oil-fired furnace. And a back garden with a lawn, flowerbeds on the sides, a pond with goldfish, water-lilies, and a copper beech tree at the end.

The phone rang and a shaky voice said,

"May I speak to Doctor Jones?"

"I'm sorry, he's on holiday."

"When will he come back?"

"In three weeks," I said.

"I can't wait that long," the voice said. "I'm going to New York tomorrow."

"Would you," I said, "like to leave a message?"

"I can't hear what you're saying," the voice said. "Can you speak up? I'm a bit deaf and have to wear a hearing aid. The doctors have a cure for this now. If I'd been born two years later I would have been all right."

"I said would you like to leave the doctor a message?"

"I don't think that will do any good," he said. "Could you look in his office and see if he has a poem of mine? It's called 'Goodbye'. If it is in proof, don't bother. I'll wait. But just find out. I am going over to teach creative writing in night school so I can make some money to come back here. The poem will probably be on the floor."

"Hold on," I said.

I went into the office at the top of the house. The floor was cluttered with papers and magazines and manuscripts with letters and envelopes attached. On a wooden table, a large snap file had correspondence. A box had cheques for small amounts. There were also several pound notes, loose change, a sheet of stamps, and two packages of cigarettes. (How trusting, I thought. The doctor doesn't know us—supposing we were crooks?) There was typing paper, large envelopes, a typewriter, a phone, telephone directories, and some galleys hanging on a nail on a wall. A smaller table had an in-and-out tray to do with his medical work, more letters, and copies of the *Lancet*. The neatest part of the room was the area where stacks of unsold copies of *ABC* were on the floor against the far wall.

"I'm sorry," I said on the phone. "I can't see it."

"Oh," he said. He sounded disappointed.

"Well, tell him that Arnold Mest called. M-E-S-T."

"I've got that," I said.

"Goodbye," he said.

"You won't guess," I told my wife. "The doctor edits a little magazine."

"We can't get away from it," she said.

Early next morning the doorbell woke us. It was the postman. He gave me several bundles. There were letters from different parts of England and Europe and air mail ones from Canada, the States,

Australia, and South America. There were two review copies of books from publishers. There were other little magazines, and what looked like medical journals, and a few bills.

As I put the envelopes and parcels on the chair in the office and saw the copies of *Horizon* and *New Writing*, the runs of *Encounter, London Magazine*, and a fine collection of contemporary books on the shelves right around the room—it brought back a time twenty years ago when I first came over.

There was still the bomb-damage to be seen, the queues, the ration books, the cigarettes under the counter. And a general seediness in people's clothes. Yet I remember it as one of my happiest times. Perhaps because we were young and full of hope and because we were so innocent of what writing involved. A lot of boys and girls had come to London from different parts. And we would meet in certain pubs, in certain restaurants, Joe Lyons, the French pub, Caves de France, the Mandrake. Then go on somewhere else. I remember going over to see another Canadian, from Montreal, who was writing a novel. He had a studio, by the Chelsea football grounds (we could always tell when a goal was scored). I remember best the cold damp winter days with the fog thick—you could just see the traffic lights—and then going inside and having some hot wine by the open fire and talking about writing, what we were writing, and where we had things out. We used to send our stories, optimistically, to the *New Yorker* and the *Atlantic*. But that was like taking a ticket in a lottery. It was the little magazines who published us, who gave encouragement and kept us going.

I remember Miss Waters. She was in her late forties, a pale woman with thinning blonde hair and a docile tabby cat. She edited a little magazine founded by her great-grandfather. She had photographs of Tennyson on the wall, of Yeats and Dylan Thomas. And wooden pigeon-holes, like the sorting room at the post office, with some of the recent back issues. She didn't know when I was coming. But she always greeted me with:

"How nice to see you. Do come in."

She walked ahead, into the dark living-room. Suggested that I take my winter coat off. Then she would bring out a decanter of sherry and fill a glass. Then take out a package of *Passing Clouds*, offer me a cigarette.

I was treated as a writer by this woman when I had very little published. And that did more than anything to keep up morale. And after another sherry, another *Passing Cloud*, and she had asked me what I was working on and seemed very interested in what I said, she told me that her great-grandfather paid Tennyson a thousand pounds for one of his short poems, and two thousand pounds to George Eliot for a short story. (Was she trying to tell me that there was money to be made out of writing?) Then she stood up. And we went into the other room. It was very neat and tidy. Magazines on a table laid out as at a newsagent's, books as in a library.

"Is there anything you would like to review?" she asked.

I would pick a novel or two, or a book of short stories.

Then she would say: "And help yourself to four books from that pile."

That pile consisted of books that she didn't want reviewed. She had told me, the first time, to take these books to a bookseller in the Strand who would give me half-price for them, and later sell them to the public libraries. But before I could get the money from him I had to sign my name in what looked like a visiting book. And I saw there, above me, the signatures of the leading Sunday and weekly reviewers—they were also selling their review copies for half-price.

And I remember how I would come to her place—with the brown envelopes lying behind the door—broke and depressed. And when I left her, I left feeling buoyed up, cheerful. There would be the few pounds from the review copies. Money enough for a hamburger and a coffee and a small cigar. And there was something to do—the books to review. She always paid in advance.

And before Miss Waters there were others. The press officer at the Norwegian Embassy—he ran a Norwegian little magazine, in English, from London. And another one, from India, also in English. My early stories appeared in both. And when I got a copy of the Indian magazine I saw that my Canadian characters had been turned into Indians. And there was another editor who would ask to borrow your box of matches. Then when you got back to your flat you found he had stuffed a pound note inside the box.

They are all gone—like their magazines.

And something has gone with them.

Those carefree days when you wrote when you felt like it. And slept in when you wanted to. And would be sure of seeing others like yourself at noon in certain places.

Now in the morning, after breakfast, I wait for the mail to come. Then I go upstairs and close the door behind me. And I make myself get on with the novel, the new story, or the article which has been commissioned by a well-paying magazine. I take a break for lunch, then come back up here until four. Once in a while I might take a day off and go on a bus to see what the country is like. I forget that there is so much colour about. Or, for a change, take a train for the day to Plymouth. But otherwise, it is up the stairs to this room. All my energy now goes into work. I light up a small Dutch cigar, and sometimes I talk to myself. I feel reasonably certain now that what I have written will be published. Writing has become my living.

Of course there are still the occasional days when things are going right and the excitement comes back from the work. Not like in those early days when writing and the life we were leading seemed so much to belong together. I had complete faith then in those little magazines. What I didn't know was that what they bred was infectious. They infected a lot of young people with the notion that to be involved with literature was somehow to be involved with the good life. And by the time you learned differently, it was usually too late.

On Friday I had to be up early. In the morning I was to be interviewed, in a rowing-boat on the Serpentine, for a Canadian television program on the "Brain-Drain". And later I was to meet my publisher for lunch.

It was very pleasant on the water early in the morning. The sun made patterns. People going to work stopped to watch. While I rowed the interviewer, the cameraman, the sound-recordist, and their equipment—and was asked why wasn't I living in Canada, and why did I write?

I met my publisher in his club. He is an American, from Boston, bald and short. We had a Martini. Then another. Then we went into the dining-room. Smoked salmon followed by duck with wine, then dessert. And ending with brandy and a large Havana cigar.

He asked me what type would I like for the book, could I send him the blurb for the dust-jacket? He told me the number of copies they would print, that one of the Sunday papers wanted to run a couple of extracts before publication. He told me some gossip about other writers, publishers, and agents. And what was I writing now? And which publishing season would he have it for?

I left him after four and caught a taxi back to the house.

"How did it go?" my wife asked.

"OK," I said. "How was the zoo?"

She began to tell me when we heard a noise. It sounded as if it was coming from the front door. We went to look and surprised a man with a key trying to open the door. He was in his late fifties, short and stocky and wearing a shabby raincoat.

"Is the doc in?" he said timidly.

"No," I said. "He's on holiday."

"Oh," he said. "I've come up from Sussex. I always have a bed here when I come up."

He spoke with an educated accent.

"I'm sorry," I said. "But we have the place for three weeks."

"I always have a bed here when I come up."

"There isn't room," I said.

"My name is George Smith," he said. "*ABC* publish me. I'm a poet."

"How do you do," I said. "We'll be gone in ten days. Come in and have a drink."

While I poured him a brandy, I asked what was the name of his last book.

He said he had enough work for a book and had sent the manuscript to—and here he named a well-known publisher.

"But I haven't heard," he said.

"That's a good sign," I said.

"Perhaps they have lost it," he said. "Or they are, like Doc, on holiday."

He brought out a small tin and took some loose tobacco and began to roll his own cigarette and one for me.

"How long," I asked, "have they had it?"

"Nearly five months," he said.

He finished his brandy. I poured him some more.

"I would ring them up and find out," I said. "Or drop them a line."

"Do you think I should?"

"Yes," I said.

I went to the door to see him out. And instead walked him to the bus stop.

The street was full of mountain ash and red berries were lying on the lawns, the sidewalk, and on the road.

"I had a letter from T. S. Eliot," he said. "I kept it all these years. But I sold it last month to Texas for fifty dollars," he said proudly. "My daughter was getting married. And I had to get her a present."

I asked him where he would stay the night.

"I have one or two other places," he said. "I come up about once every six weeks. London is my commercial centre."

I went and bought him a package of cigarettes.

"Thank you," he said.

The red bus came and I watched him get on.

When I got back my wife said, "Well, do you feel better?"

"No," I said.

It went on like this—right through the time we were there. An assortment of people turned up at the door. There was a young blonde girl—she wanted to lick stamps for literature. There were visiting lecturers and professors from American and Canadian and English universities. There were housewives; one said, over the phone, "I'll do anything to get into print." There were long-distance telephone calls. One rang after midnight and woke us up. "Nothing important," the voice said. "I just wanted to have a talk. We usually do now and then. I've had stories in *ABC*."

There was, it seemed, a whole world that depended on the little magazine.

I tried to be out of the house as much as possible. I went to see my agent. He had a cheque for four hundred dollars, less his commission, waiting for me, for the sale of a story. He took me out for a meal. And we talked about the size of advances, the sort of money paperback publishers were paying these days, the way non-fiction was selling better than fiction. I met other writers in expensive clubs and restaurants. We gossiped about what middle-aged writer was leaving his middle-aged wife to live with a young girl. And what publisher was leaving his firm to form his own house. I was told what magazines were starting—who paid the best.

Then I would come back to the phone ringing, the piles of mail, and people turning up at the door eager to talk about the aesthetics of writing. I didn't mind the young. But it was the men and women who were around my age or older who made me uncomfortable. I didn't like the feeling of superiority I had when I was with them. Or was it guilt? I didn't know.

Meanwhile my wife and kids enjoyed themselves. They went to the Victoria and Albert Museum, the National Gallery, the Tate. And came back with postcard reproductions that they sent to friends. They went to a couple of Proms, to a play, had a day in Richmond Park, Hampton Court, and a boat ride on the Thames.

When the time came to go back—they didn't want to.

But I did.

I had passed through my *ABC* days. And I wanted to get away. Was it because it was a reminder of one's youth? Or of a time which promised more than it turned out to be? I told myself that there was an unreality about it all—that our lives then had no economic base —that it was a time of limbo. But despite knowing these things, I carry it with me. It represents a sort of innocence that has gone.

On the Saturday morning waiting for the taxi to come to take us to Paddington Station, the phone rang. And a young girl's voice wanted to know about her short story.

I said the doctor was away. He would be back later. She ought to ring this evening.

"What time?"

"After nine," I said.

"Have you read the story?" she asked. "What do you think of it?"

"We just rented the house," I said. "We were here for a holiday."

"Oh," she said. "You're not one of us?"

"No," I said.

Then the taxi came. And the driver began to load the cases into the back of the car.

NATHAN COHEN

The conversation between Nathan Cohen and the novelist Joyce Cary was recorded in Oxford, England, in September, 1956, and broadcast on Anthology in January, 1957. Cary died in March, 1957, and the text of the interview was published in Issue 3 of the Tamarack Review *(Spring, 1957).*

This interview was one of several that Nathan Cohen recorded for Anthology *on a visit to England in 1956. He also talked at that time to Evelyn Waugh, Iris Murdoch, Walter Allen, and F. R. Leavis, among other writers. Nathan Cohen's long association with the CBC went back at least to 1948. He reviewed theatre and sometimes books and films for various radio programs, was a script editor with CBC television drama, and was perhaps best known as chairman of* Fighting Words *on both television and radio. At the time of his death in 1971 he was drama critic for the* Toronto Star.

❖

A Conversation with Joyce Cary

COHEN: Mr. Cary, about a year or so ago the issue of censorship was a very lively and vexatious issue here among writers in England, but now the sound and fury seems to have died. Is the censorship problem ended?

CARY: Well, I don't think it is. It's only gone underground. What's happening now is that the publishers are refusing books that they think are going to get into trouble. And I think there is still a very strong movement for censorship coming on. For instance, about a week ago the police impounded thousands and thousands of postcards. No question of whether they're right or not—I mean, that has to be decided. It's a very powerful movement for censorship.

COHEN: Who composes this movement for censorship?

CARY: It's a mixed movement of the churches, partly—a section of the churches. A very large section of the left wing in England is Evangelical and they are strongly inclined at any rate to centralized government, to ruling by government decree, and that in time means censorship. And also they're mostly people who don't care twopence about the arts.

COHEN: What kind of books are they particularly anxious to censor?

CARY: Well, that's the amusing thing. They're just anxious to stop anything they don't happen to like. And so they attack almost any book. For instance, one bench of magistrates ordered that Boccaccio should be put on the fire. The joke is that a lot of Boccaccio is very censorable. It raised the whole question. As a matter of fact, I wrote to a paper about it—*The Times*—and Boccaccio was reprieved. But logically the censors were right; it ought to have been burned.

COHEN: Do you think there is a case to be made for censorship?

CARY: No, I think none whatever. There is a case to be made for not exposing in shop-windows books or statues or anything else that might offend people. There could be a case against offending people in ordinary goings about. There is absolutely no case for censoring any publication in private.

COHEN: The thing that I have noted with regard to the issue of censorship is the division of feeling between the publishers and the authors. I gather that the publishers are inclined to go along as much as they can with the forces of censorship.

CARY: Publishers are apt of course to save themselves trouble, and —still more sinister in England—the booksellers' associations are rather inclined to do that. A small bookseller wants to know where he is. In England a great many booksellers are genuinely devoted to good literature and want to sell it. There are, of course, an enormous number who are not—shops selling more or less paperbacks. They want to know where they are and they don't care a bit about what they sell. They just want to make the money. And they are always ready for censorship.

COHEN: I was thinking, too, of the kind of publisher who, when an author brings a novel to him, says, in effect: "There are passages here, or there is something in the tone of it that is liable to bring us into the courts"—and, in effect, prevents the writer from writing in that way.

CARY: Actually there's a great deal of that now.

COHEN: There is?

CARY: A lot of publishers *are* saying: "Well, we're very sorry but we can't take a chance on this book." In fact, you can't expect anything else from a publisher. I mean, he's a man in business. A great many English publishers do spend a lot of money and take big risks on starting new authors, but they are not going to chance it in law—chance being fined on the most irresponsible evidence. For instance, in the case against Heinemann's, the counsel said to the jury: "Would you allow this book to be read by your daughter of twenty-five? He didn't say "your son of twenty-five". It's absolutely a plea to the purest kind of prejudice, and not only that but old-fashioned sex prejudice. He didn't say: "Would you allow your son of twenty-five. . .?" but he said "your daughter of twenty-five".

COHEN: This is a matter decided by jury, I take it. I thought it was up to the judges to decide.

CARY: No, it's a jury case. Does it have a corrupting influence? That's a miserable criterion of judgement—corrupting influence. People can corrupt themselves with anything if they like.

COHEN: The pure in heart can't be corrupted. Those who aren't can easily be corrupted.

CARY: Quite so.

COHEN: Mr. Cary, let's move on to another subject which I'm very anxious to speak to you about, sir, and which ties in with something you said at the beginning of the interview, or at least indirectly. You were referring to the churches. It's been my observation that there has been a great return, if you like, to a quest for religion among professional writers both in North America and in England, in the English-speaking countries. Have you gone through this kind of experience?

CARY: Well, I did return to religion pretty early on.

COHEN: You say you returned to it. You mean you were an atheist before?

CARY: Oh, yes. I was brought up in the Church of England and at my private school I was quite pious. At my public school I was confirmed. But while I was being prepared for confirmation I asked various questions about the incarnation, especially about the problem of evil. And I got very poor answers.

COHEN: Answers from your parents?

CARY: No, from the man at school who was preparing me. I had no mother. I had lost my mother then, and religion wasn't much of a subject at home. But at the same time that my masters were teaching me to ask questions, this man refused to answer them about religion, and I suppose it planted some kind of doubt in my mind. Because very soon afterwards my faith faded right away.

And I became what I called an agnostic—which is really a completely illogical position.

COHEN: Why do you say that?

CARY: Well, a man can't be an agnostic, he's simply a neutralist. He's not taking up any place at all about a vital question. A man is either a behaviourist—he says the world's a machine, and none of us are free—or he's a theist. If he has a sense of any goodness in the world, even the smallest good act, unselfish act, that's ever done, he has to be a theist. Because the world has stopped being a machine. I mean the world can't be a cash register if it feels goodness and feels love and understands beauty.

COHEN: But you were an agnostic?

CARY: I called myself an agnostic for years. But of course I went to an art school and learned aesthetic judgement, and when I began to write I found I hadn't got a sensible answer to the world. On the one side I spoke of beauty, which is an emotion, a personal emotion. I acknowledged personality in the world, in human nature and in universal nature. I acknowledged personal feelings and yet I made no count of them. I called myself an agnostic and behaved as if the world were a machine. I had the two things to deal with. On one hand science, scientific judgement; on the other hand personal emotion, which has nothing to do with science.

COHEN: You separate them completely?

CARY: They had nothing to do in direct experience. Science uses machines. Science treats the body as a machine—examines the working of the machine. It has to, that's its job. But psychology—as a novelist I had to deal with personal feelings, with a man as a personal, feeling soul. So I had these two elements. And what I'd done before—I rationalized my position by throwing out one element and saying: "I'm not going to tend to the personal side. I accept the world as a machine." And I'd be an agnostic and say: "Oh well, it works like a machine. I'll take it like that." And now I found it was senseless. I had no regular idea of the world. I had to get one. So I accepted both things. I said I've only got to go on direct experience. I'm quite sure about these things. I'm sure of science. I believe in science. Therefore miracles are impossible. You cannot have miracles if you accept scientific research. On the other hand, I accept the existence of goodness, of love, of beauty—I accept these things, and therefore there is personality too. And I didn't attempt to reconcile the two things. I accepted them for some time and I have reconciled them since.

COHEN: Then you feel that they can be considered as a unity.

CARY: Oh, undoubtedly; but then if you want to go into metaphysics, I can give you the position.

COHEN: Go into metaphysics, Mr. Cary.

CARY: Well, what I say is that if you admit a personal God in the world he very soon occupies the whole ground. He's obviously the most important thing. We live for our emotions and He dominates the world. Very well. How can you therefore explain evil in the world and the mechanism of the mechanical part of life? Well, we are told by the philosophers that a thing that exists must be something. It must have a character. And therefore I say that the world we know as a character—its reality depends on a fixed character. And God's only existence therefore as a real existing being depends on a fixed character in being. Aquinas will tell you all the things God can't do. It's quite accepted in theology that God has limitations. He can't change the past, for instance; He can't do evil. There are a lot of things God can't do. I think there are nine that St. Thomas tells us God can't do.

COHEN: Would you say that this acceptance of God, this recognition of him, is at the centre of a man—let's say like Gully Jimson or Chester Nimmo?

CARY: Gully Jimson in his book is accepting the aesthetic God. (I didn't put any metaphysics in there directly; it's full of metaphysics indirectly.) When he says this is pure horsemeat, you see, the horse's mouth is the mouth of God, the voice of God as known to an artist. Why should a man waste his life in seeking to paint pictures, in seeking beauty—so many mysterious purposes? Why should he starve himself? Why should he behave just like any religious maniac in pursuit of a certain kind of composition, a certain arrangement of colours? It doesn't belong to the mechanical world. It belongs to a very mysterious world in which God, the God of beauty, dominates his soul, his character, and his life.

COHEN: And Sarah, what about Sarah?

CARY: Sarah is a simple woman in her own book who is full of affection. She's always trying to build her nest, and as Gully complains, she's always trying to build it around some man and build him into it. But she is pure, simple, affectionate.

COHEN: There is one aspect (if we may come back to religion for a moment) of your experience that's rather at odds with perhaps a great number of your contemporaries, and that is that when they became, if you like, converted, they went from atheism or agnosticism as the case may be to Roman Catholicism, rather than to what I take to be Protestantism in your case. Why to Protestantism rather than Roman Catholicism?

CARY: Well, the reason may have been that I was already Church of England and simply returned to that Church. It has been said, and I think very truly, that Catholicism is a religion and Protestantism is a faith. What's important about the Catholic religion is their ritual, their rules, the forms of their life. It's a fine religion, but it is religion. And many Catholics are quite good Catholics with very little faith—exerting very little faith. But the essence of Protestantism is its faith. And that's why you get Protestants continually breaking up and very often forming sects which practically have no religion at all—just two or three people who meet together to read the Bible and talk to each other—who still have this deep faith. Protestantism is a faith, and what I needed was faith.

COHEN: Is it because of your feeling of need for faith that you live in a city like Oxford and find your friends and companionship to a large extent among philosophers and teachers?

CARY: Well, I came here originally because our Irish house had been sold up, we hadn't got an Irish house any more, and my wife's brother was a don here. And there's a very good school, one of the best schools in the world here for small boys, and I had four small boys to educate. That was the chief reason why I came here. But also I had friends in the colleges, and since then I have gone on living here for all these years, over thirty years, because it is such a delightful place to live in.

COHEN: Don't you find that it takes you somewhat out of the stream of literary activities in England?

CARY: I am, I suppose, very much out of the literary stream.

COHEN: Doesn't this disturb you?

CARY: That doesn't disturb me at all. I think you see a great many writers in England have lived away from that stream—Conrad lived in the depths of the country. It's true, I suppose, that Henry James discussed literature to a certain extent, but I think he much more discussed life. And I'm much more interested in talking about life and morals and politics and so on (as my friends here are)—and even scholarship—than in discussing books and purely literary problems.

COHEN: One of the things that fascinates me about your books, and I use the word "fascinate" quite deliberately, is your ability to present a story from the individual viewpoint of your central character, as in the case of Gully, Sarah, Chester, or any of these people. Now I'm not going to ask you to speak about the imaginative process, but how are you able to bring to bear and sustain this individual's point of view?

CARY: Well, of course, I've always been interested in individuals. As I say, I'm more interested in life than in books and I'm more interested in people than books. And every writer must have the power of entering into another person. Think how, when you are writing dialogue, you have to be two different people instantaneously. I mean you have to be a different person perhaps ten times on a page. You can't stop and say each time: "Now what sort of a chap is this and how would he talk?" You have to be that person. And in the same way, in a more extended way, you enter into your characters right through a book. But why I should have that power to any excess, that I don't know.

COHEN: You mentioned in an article you wrote once that there was a period of ten years or so of your life when you found yourself unable to write. I presume that this was near the start of your career as a writer.

CARY: Yes, I was educating myself, re-educating myself at the beginning, because as I say I had no settled faith when I began to write. And when you invent characters and make them talk, you very soon find out what you don't know. You're stopped at once by a character when he's talking and you say: "Now what does this fellow really mean by that?" And you have to find out what you mean. You very soon discover your own ignorance, if you invent characters and make them talk, and I found that out. And having had to acquire a faith and having had to get for myself some reconciled idea of why the world could be both a machine and a personal soul, or rather why it could present that double appearance (because they're both phenomenal; they both aren't just appearances), why it could represent these appearances—that meant a lot of work and a lot of thought.

COHEN: And the moment you achieved this kind of thing, this, I suppose, would be the turning-point in your life.

CARY: Since then I have written too many books—I mean I write books too easily. I've got more unpublished novels than published ones.

COHEN: Writing is not difficult for you, Mr. Cary?

CARY: Absolutely easy. My difficulty is to choose between the stuff I write.

COHEN: How do you choose?

CARY: Well, that's very difficult to say. I don't really choose until I come to write a new book. Then I read all these books that are half done and decide then. I've got an American scholar that's writing a book about me now, Professor Andrew Wright, and he's been working on my manuscripts for the last six months.

He's been telling me about some of my early beginnings I've forgotten. He is continually coming in and saying, "Do you remember a novel called so-and-so?" and I can't even remember the name. Half-written novel.

COHEN: What's this book you're working on now? You mentioned it—

CARY: I'm working on a book about religion now. Because I've dealt with all different angles in my world, the world as I see it, in my special philosophy of life, the world of creative freedom— the world of creative freedom and its effect on the world. I've written all the different angles on that. I've written the political angle; I've written it from the point of view, in *A Fearful Joy*, of change due to mechanical invention, mechanical transport; in *The Moonlight* I've dealt with it from the point of view of the woman's world, the world that is wished on woman by her sex, whether she likes it or not. However she may face that world, that is the fundamental factor in her life. I have written one book on religion, but that was in a political trilogy; it was done from a political point of view. Now I'm writing a book about religion purely as religious people feel it.

COHEN: Your central character's a religious man?

CARY: My central character's a religious man. All my central characters are religious people.

COHEN: One other question I would like to ask you about, Mr. Cary, and I'm just wondering how I should put it. Religion or the resolution of religious vexations has been the chief turning-point in your life. Who have been the main influences, though, personally? Have there been influences in your life that have affected you to almost the same extent, perhaps, as your search for, and finding of, a faith?

CARY: Well, I wouldn't be aware of them. I've had influences from all sides. Conrad was a very powerful influence.

COHEN: Did you know Conrad?

CARY: No, I didn't know him, but his books were a very powerful influence when I was a young man: his very strong sense of honour, his dignity, his own whole moral sense, his whole approach to life. He was a powerful influence. Henry James was another, with his very, very strong sense of the moral world and especially his sense of the fragility of innocence—that everything good, everything true, everything beautiful, was by that very fact especially exposed to danger and destruction.

COHEN: And usually destructible, surely.

CARY: Yes. In his books, usually destroyed. And another influence was Hardy—Hardy, with his sense of tragic fate. Those three in literature were three of the most powerful influences in my life.

COHEN: And you found in them the kind of outlook or the kind of sense of direction that you as a person, as a writer, respond to.

CARY: I responded partly to them, to their moral influence, their moral force. Tolstoy was another. The Russians—Dostoevsky was another. Dostoevsky, of course, was a man who could never make up his mind, a divided man. He said if Christ was on one side and truth was on the other, he'd have to follow Christ. He's a fascinating study of the split mind.

COHEN: You've read all Dostoevsky?

CARY: I've read all Dostoevsky, yes. There's a wonderful passage in *The Brothers Karamazov* where he defeats himself. He puts up a man who's going to be defeated. Ivan is going to argue and is going to be defeated by the Christian apologist. But Ivan talks so well that he knocks the Christian apologist right out. It was Dostoevsky again; he couldn't help swallowing the truth. Although he wanted Christ to win, when he was writing, he followed the truth. Got himself into an awful jam that way. Because the Public Prosecutor nearly got after him.

COHEN: Do you ever feel that you are going to run into censorship problems yourself?

CARY: Oh, I'm on the index in Ireland now—in Eire. And I daresay elsewhere. In Spain—they used to translate me, but Spain has just stopped my last books.

COHEN: There is one other thing I'd like to speak to you about, Mr. Cary. You came into your career fairly late. I mean you were no youngster when you first started writing or getting published. And you have in the last period achieved a considerable reputation in a critical sense, you are accepted, you are regarded as one of the leading, if not perhaps *the* leading English novelist alive today. Does the fact that you are so rated, that you are categorized, that somebody is writing a book about you, does it matter to you?

CARY: I think it matters. Oh yes, praise matters a lot. And what has mattered to me enormously are my fans, intelligent fans. Every now and again you get a very intelligent letter, and you know you've got through to people; that matters a lot. The general sort of reputation—you never know what your reputation is. Years ago—ten years ago—I was told I was the greatest novelist, and nobody else agreed with it—it was what some critic wrote. But how do you judge your reputation? I mean cuttings come in from here and there repeating very much the same sort of judgement, obviously copying each other. Your only judgement of what you've really achieved is the critical answer from intelligent people, people whose judgement you trust.

COHEN: And your own feelings, your own judgements?

CARY: Well, your own feelings about a book, my feelings about a book, are never very satisfactory, because when you read a book yourself you see what you've done wrong. And all this is disappointing, naturally. I mean, when you're starting a book you've got a fine theme, you've got your character, you think it's going to be a wonderful masterpiece. It's always disappointing, you always run into snags.

COHEN: You start off with a definite theme? You don't write and sort of watch the characters and the incident grow?

CARY: Well, I start off with a universal theme. I mean I've got the theme about my whole view of life—that's what my theme is. I always start off with a character in a certain situation and I'm taking them all the time. I've taken sometimes from life. Sometimes I think about them and write them down and these little sketches may sometimes develop into a short story. I never know. And they sometimes may begin a novel. If they develop, say, beyond a short-story length, I say: "Well, this ought to be a novel. It's too big stuff for a short story." So when I start a novel, as I say, I don't know when it's going to be a novel, and when I finish the novel I'm doing now, for the next one I'll pick up one of these things I've already got, perhaps twenty or thirty thousand words. I won't know where it started originally.

COHEN: Does it mean much to you if posterity remembers you?

CARY: I should think so. I should like to think I shall be remembered. I should like to think I'll be read, because every writer is an evangelist. I am essentially putting something over that I want to be understood. And I want to have an effect because I think it's true. I think my view of life is true. Otherwise I wouldn't be writing about it. And I want it to be understood.

COHEN: Mr. Cary, I will ask you one more question. It's a highly impertinent question, and if you don't want to answer it, tell me, and it will simply be cut out of the broadcast. Are you afraid of dying?

CARY: No, I don't think anybody's afraid of dying. You may be afraid of any pain you may get on the way, you may wonder how you're going to stand what's coming to you. And you may rather hope to die suddenly, and quickly, and without knowing about it.

I don't think anybody's afraid of dying. I've been dead already as a matter of fact. I was killed in the first war.

COHEN: You were shot in the ear?

CARY: I was shot in the...well...the mastoid. I got a bullet that scraped my mastoid, and of course it felt as if my brains were blown to pieces, and knocked me right out. And I just sat down to think: "Well, this is it, and it is easy."

COHEN: You're a very remarkable man, sir.

JOYCE MARSHALL

Joyce Marshall, who lives in Toronto, is a writer, translator, and freelance editor. Among her translations were three books by Gabrielle Roy— The Road Past Altamont, Windflower, *and* Enchanted Summer *—and she won the Canada Council Translation Prize in 1976 for her translation of* Enchanted Summer. *For a number of years she worked as a freelance editor —always sympathetic to new writers—for* Anthology. *"A Private Place" was broadcast on the program in 1973 and was the title story of a collection of Joyce Marshall's short fiction published in 1975 by Oberon Press.*

❖

A Private Place

Even Berit seemed to think he might not feel too happy about moving so soon into the dead man's apartment. Or perhaps she was just trying to make a good impression on Hanne. You could never quite tell about Berit. Lars couldn't, even after ten years. She could be so hideously outspoken and then fret about appearances before some stranger. For there the two of them sat, assuring him with what appeared to be equal concern that it wasn't as if Hanne's father had had the fatal heart attack in the apartment. He had been stricken in the elevator. Someone on a higher floor had rung. The elevator came up, the door opened and there, his medical bag at his side, lay Arne Svensen—in a huddle Hanne hoped had not been too grotesque or foolish. Her father was a proud man. Had been, she amended, biting her lip. Damn Berit anyway, Lars thought. She was always so central to every scene; he'd almost forgotten that this transfer of the apartment had an entirely different sense for Hanne. Till then he'd been feeling half amused by Berit's enterprise. She'd read of Dr. Svensen's death in the paper, remembered an old friendship with his daughter, who lived in Hammerfest and could have no possible use for a bachelor apartment in Oslo, had confronted her, for all Lars knew, at the graveside. At any rate, he'd found them drinking coffee, the matter almost settled, when he came home from what Berit had taken to calling his "piddling little job at the shipping company". And Hanne didn't even want key money, Berit informed him proudly, as if this reflected credit on her. As perhaps it did. Lars just had to buy Arne Svensen's share in the building and most of the furniture; she'd already arranged terms with Hanne and he could move in that very night.

Well, that was how apartments were found in Norway, had been for as long as Lars remembered. If there hadn't been a housing shortage, there might never have been a marriage. He'd wanted to leave home and been flattered when Berit, who was three years older and independently well-off, invited him to share the big, rather grand apartment she'd inherited from an aunt. Charmed too by Berit's gay and astringent tongue, round little freckled face and romping ways in bed. When she became pregnant a year or so later, they'd been surprised to find they wanted the child and had married. And loved each other by then, he believed; at any rate, they were a couple and very much wound in and around one another. The housing shortage had perhaps even wrecked the marriage. If he could have moved out at once the year before when Berit first said he bored her and she wanted him to go. . .well, she might have missed him and agreed to continue the marriage until their child grew up. But after all the fruitless leads and near-misses —for even Berit couldn't insist he go back to live with his mother— and having to listen to her railing at this failure, unusual for her, to bend things and people to her whim, their marriage was quite finished, it was dead. He was as sure—and as glad—as she was.

"But hell, what's all this about going tonight?" he said, as much out of principle as anything else. "After all, there are all sorts of— Where *is* Kristi, by the way?"

Berit told him that their daughter, now eight, was having dinner with a friend, then added with a softness he hadn't seen for many months, "I don't want her to see you packing and leaving. She can come to you Sunday for the day. That will be better for her. And you *must* go tonight, Lars. We owe this favour to Hanne."

For Hanne had to return to Hammerfest the next morning. She wanted to show him the one or two bits of family furniture she would send for. Not only that. Her father's secretary, who had cleaned out the papers and most of the clothing and crated the books, had put aside a few things for Hanne. And she couldn't bear to go there alone.

Unceremonious as this was, Lars felt as he packed his clothes and arranged with Berit about having his books picked up, it was something at least that he could do a service for Hanne. It made the whole thing more human. She seemed like a nice girl, even though buck-toothed. An honest sort of girl, not ashamed to admit her grief. And not stupid either. She hadn't missed Berit's pleased little grin the moment she got her way.

So he was with Hanne when she discovered the red windbreaker.

"I didn't know Father had a mistress," she said faintly when it turned up inside an old ski jacket of Arne Svensen's that was one of the things she was taking to Hammerfest.

"Oh...just someone who came to see him," said Lars. "And forgot it. Or...could it have been your mother's?" Her mother had died only six months previously, just before Arne Svensen moved into this place.

Hanne shook her head, searching for a label. "Schwartz Sportswear, Toronto," she read almost in a question. "I have an uncle there. My father visited him once."

"Well—" Lars said, unable to handle the mystery of this garment that had been so obviously hidden, sleeves inside sleeves. "It's probably quite innocent. Take it and wear it. It would suit you."

"Oh no," said Hanne, shocked, and seemed about to hang it on a peg in the hallway.

"Then take it and give it away," he said.

So she folded it back inside her father's old washed blue jacket and put both with some photograph albums and other trifles in her shopping bag.

Chiefly to annoy Berit, he had removed their last bottle of wine from the kitchen so he was able to offer Hanne a drink, which she accepted. He was anxious not to be alone, not yet, and had an idea that they might talk, he would tell her of his worries about Kristi; Hanne would understand and a little later he might kiss her. But she kept twisting her glass, which after all belonged to her father, and when she stood up suddenly and said she had to go, he didn't try to stop her. And as soon as he had closed the door and was alone with Arne Svensen's furniture and crated books, he began to feel stiff and weak, as if he had been whipped and as he was to feel for many months to come.

And there was all the embarrassment of telling people he'd moved out, some of them so surprised, others so clearly not surprised. And which was worse he didn't know. Even more difficult was informing his mother, who replied with a recital of Berit's shortcomings, all of them linked in some way with spinelessness in himself. He listened and made allowances as he had been doing for as long as he could remember. She was a trying woman but she was not well—submerged in mawkish self-pity, Berit always said. Perhaps, but there was undeniably still pain in the back she'd broken jumping out of the second-floor window with Lars in her arms. "Quick, quick, get the boy out," his father had said. Lars sometimes thought he remembered the thudding at the door and those words, then the leap and other sounds from behind as his mother crawled, half holding him and sobbing, to the next house. ("You couldn't possibly remember, you were only two," Berit always said and "Well, so he was a hero. But did any of it—his getting himself shot, not to mention your mother's ruined back and disposition and life—bring the end of the war one second closer?") It had been partly this—Berit's ability to put into words what he himself could think but never say—that had drawn him to her; she'd made such a cool, pleasant change from his mother.

Then came Sunday and trying to give Kristi a nice day. He saw that he was going to have to plan to entertain the child, who seemed uncomfortable and even timid in the strange surroundings. If it had been summer they could have gone to one of the beaches and in winter they'd ski but on this brief raining November day two people, one eight and one thirty-three—even a father and daughter who'd always enjoyed one another—couldn't just sit in a one-room apartment and talk. He had to offer something. So he bought her dinner in the little restaurant downstairs and that made it a bit of a party.

With all this, and finding a lawyer to handle his side of the separation, he didn't have much time to think about Dr. Svensen's mail. Hanne hadn't left him an address and he was damned if he'd ask Berit, who probably didn't know anyway; the friendship had been vague, he suspected, and simply revived for the occasion. So he stacked the dead man's letters on his desk, which sooner or later carters were to take by road and sea to Hammerfest. Circulars, magazines, what appeared to be notices of meetings; the old man seemed to have had fairly wide interests for a doctor. Then an airmail letter with Canadian stamps and three days later another. They were similarly typed and couldn't be from Hanne's uncle who'd have known, at least when the second was mailed, that his brother was dead. By the time the cartage men showed up, there were four of those letters—the third three weeks after the second, the fourth the next day. He couldn't follow his original plan of sending all the mail in a packet with the desk. So he scratched "deceased" across the other envelopes and consigned them to the post office. The Canadian letters, which had no return address and would have been opened by some clerk, he put in the back of the kitchen drawer beneath Arne Svensen's stainless steel; Hanne had said her father was a proud man. And he couldn't forget the puzzled look on her face as she said, "I didn't know Father had a mistress." Protecting her, this grown woman with a husband and two children, he was in some way protecting Kristi, he felt. Or if not protecting, setting up a fund that others could draw on in the future to save his daughter from something it would be unpleasant for her to know. Such fancies, a sense even of being watched—he didn't ask by what or whom—were very frequent in those days.

A week later Hanne wrote to inform him of the safe arrival of the desk and books. She'd just realized that she'd forgotten to give the post office directions about her father's mail. She assumed that if anything important had come, Lars would have sent it along. Most mail nowadays was junk; a shame to slaughter the trees. And then in a postscript, too casually: Had anyone inquired about the red windbreaker? She had it still.

That worried him. He thought of various stories to tell her. The jacket had been left by her father's secretary when she sorted the papers and clothes. No good; the relieved and rather earnest Hanne would promptly mail it to the woman. One of the tenants had discarded it and offered it to Arne Svensen for her. Unlikely. In all these weeks he hadn't said more than good-day to any of them; he doubted that Arne Svensen had either. It was that kind of building; working people, a few couples but mostly single men and women, including a number of men of his own age, newly separated or divorced, he supposed, who had left the larger apartments to their wives. He sometimes saw one or other of them in the elevator with their children on Sundays when he was bringing Kristi. The children eyed one another, which was more than their fathers did. Living so close in this big country—now in their little apartments as formerly in valley-troughs between the mountains—Norwegians learned early to keep to their own space. Otherwise life would become intolerable. He accepted this.

In the end he didn't answer Hanne's letter though for a long time he believed he would—when he had thought of a sensible explanation for the jacket. (Damn it, he shouldn't have problems of this sort now when his own life was in such chaos. Berit, with that sense of the dramatic that was her charm and her tyranny, was being tormenting about the settlement and access to Kristi. She had even poisoned several of their friends against him with stories they wouldn't repeat.) Occasionally he took out the blue thin envelopes

—five by the time Hanne's letter came and in the week before Christmas a sixth. Several times he held each up to the light—in case an address appeared, he told himself, but nothing did; she used only one side of the sheets. How steadily she loved that old man and kept on writing, after many would have been too hurt to continue. He saw her as a young girl and very pretty. And Arne must have been—well, Hanne was certainly thirty, which put her father at least in his fifties. It was unjust that he should have commanded all this love whereas Lars had simply drifted into a ridiculous attachment and marriage with Berit, who in her search for originality refused to like skiing or outdoor life like a real Norwegian, professed to be sexy and deeply maternal but was actually scheming, even mischievous. And at the core deeply disappointed—disappointed among other things, he had to admit, in him.

It was rather unsatisfactory Christmas. Berit wouldn't hear of his having Kristi for Christmas Eve so he had to dine alone with his mother, who devoted most of the meal to another listing of Berit's faults and reiterations of how much she missed her only grandchild. She probably did but she could very well have saved the dinner and tree till the next day. First Christmas, when he was to have Kristi. However, she was a great traditionalist and refused. So he and his daughter took the long tram ride up to the restaurant at Frognerseteren and it was a trifle flat. The big log room was almost empty—Norwegians simply didn't eat out at this season and those present looked like foreign embassy people—and a thin but steady salt of snow muffled the view. He wished he were another sort and could offer wine to these strangers but he did all he could, bowing and smiling at everyone when he went out. The strangers looked pleased and one man, an American, came over to offer what he called "compliments of the season" and to stroke Kristi's silvery sleek head.

"Next time we'll ski," Lars told her as they went around to Berit's, and the child seemed pleased with the idea. That smooth and perfectly moulded little face—not apple-shaped like Berit's or long-chinned like his own and his mother's. She must look like his father, he thought, finding it odd that this had never occurred to him before. Or was it so odd? Perhaps such a thing just couldn't have occurred to him while he was with Berit. He'd had his picture of his father, classic and strong with no relation to the grainy snapshot by his mother's bed. Now he saw him as gentler, with some of the completeness and serenity that amazed him in his daughter.

For two weeks after New Year's there were no airmail letters for Arne Svensen. She knows now, Lars thought with grief for her; the old man wouldn't have failed to send her word at Christmas if he were alive.

He himself was very busy during those weeks. Kristi turned up for skiing in boots that were much too small; thank heaven he noticed it before they were on the slopes. Berit insisted that the new pair was his problem. So he had to go around the shops after work with a drawing of the child's feet; it took two tries to get a pair that was quite right. But it was worth it. They spent three wonderful hours in the woods outside the city. Kristi was beautifully co-ordinated and had the makings of a fine skier; he'd arrange slalom lessons for her in a year or so. Meanwhile he was sufficient teacher and he'd make sure she grew up loving the woods and outdoor life. They spoke little but were happy. The sun was still low but it would rise in the marvellous Norwegian way almost visibly from day to day like a balloon; their hours in the woods would grow longer. By Easter...or perhaps he could arrange leave during the February school-holiday week and take her to Geilo or even to the high moon-plateau of Finse, somewhere special.

The next evening there was another flimsy blue envelope in his box. And this one had an address in the upper corner. So now it would end, he thought as he set his piece of cod to boil for his dinner. He just had to put the letters in a big envelope with a note. But how would he begin? Dear Apartment 476? To whom it may concern? Dear Miss—? All sounded hopelessly cruel when the next words were going to have to be, "I regret to inform you..." Try as he might, the letter would be clumsy. He spoke English stiffly, he knew, and wrote it even more stiffly. And without a proper salutation...

He worried about it all evening and for the next two days, trying out various modes of address, feeling increasingly inept about what should have been a simple thing. And then his lawyer phoned him at work to say that Berit was adamant; she would allow him only two Sundays a month with Kristi though he wanted four or three. He came home and cooked a meal. The hours dragged. He still hadn't got a phone; nothing could come into this emptiness. (Other people pulled strings and by-passed the waiting-list. Berit would have been able to.) He had not been troubled particularly by living with furniture and pictures that had been chosen by a dead man, he had moved, after all, from his mother's choice of house-hold goods to Berit's. Now the chairs and the lamps accused him. At ten o'clock he knew what he must do: Open one of the letters and look quickly at the signature; then he could write "Dear Miss Elizabeth" or whatever it was. He took the blue tissue envelopes from their present resting-place in his bedside table—the kitchen had become too messy and Kristi might have found them—sorted them by date-stamp, earliest on top, and opened that (which he could explain had been an error). Her name was Margaret—he liked that, it fitted her, pronounced in the Norwegian way with equal syllables. Some words caught him and he was reading; it was just a note—she was used now to being home but missed Arne Svensen dreadfully, she was waiting for a letter. Three days later— for without conscious intention he had opened the second envelope —it had come; she referred to things they had done in Oslo, told him how much she liked the apartment, it was so much nicer than hers or anything to be found in Toronto. So she had been here so recently with the old man, had slept with him presumably in that alcove-bed where he now slept, Lars was thinking as he went on opening and reading. The third letter, after a three-week gap, acknowledged a letter with pictures; Arne Svensen might not have put on enough stamps, it had gone surface mail. She didn't ridicule him for this, Lars noted, just stated it simply. Her fourth letter of a day later—here it came finally, the red windbreaker—Arne Svensen needn't mail it to her; as long as it was hanging there, she'd have to go back to get it. Her fifth letter expressed some confusion about the crossing of letters, it seemed to her that he now owed her two or three, and only the Christmas note admitted anxiety; she hoped Arne Svensen hadn't caught the flu that was raging all over the world. And in this latest letter the address on the envelope was the only hint of fear. They seemed to have been corresponding for a number of years; there had been other spaces, finally explained by postal inefficiency or what seemed a frequent failure by the old man to use enough stamps. Silly old fool, Lars thought: Why didn't he leave a note that this girl was to be notified when he died? Did he think he'd live forever?

And then he realized the shamefulness of what he'd done. Worse, he'd made it impossible to return the letters; they couldn't all have been "opened in error". He'd have to wait now for the next one and send that back without reference to the others, as if he'd just moved into the apartment. He folded the tissue sheets back in their envelopes and put them away among his socks.

That night he tossed in the narrow bed where Arne Svensen and Margaret had lain. And when he slept, he was skiing with Margaret in her red windbreaker, looping down the long hill below Frogner-seteren. They slalomed closely and in unison as if there were music playing and her loose black hair whipped across his face; he wondered when he awakened why he had not tried to touch her.

Next day as he was eating his lunch sandwiches at his desk, without thought or plan he dialed Berit's number and asked her to take him back. "A second chance," he said as her silence grew.

"Lars dear," she said finally, "I *gave* you a second chance. It lasted for two years."

"You mean for two whole years—" His voice rose, his co-workers could hear him, he didn't care. "You mean you were testing—Why didn't you tell me?"

She gave one of her familiar shrieks of laughter. "Would you have tried harder, Lars? Would you have been able to please me? Or just become more solemn, more tiresome, more—?"

He hung up, thinking he must be losing what little sense he had. He was spending too much time alone. And he was bored. Whether in a good mood or bad, Berit had kept things interesting. And because she quickly tired of people, there was always someone new about the flat. His building had a nice common-room that tenants could use for parties. He'd put himself down for the first free Saturday, splurge on catering, invite everyone he knew. He decided a little later that this was too grand a way to start; he'd never given a party on his own. Instead he'd invite a few couples for after-dinner coffee—a week from Sunday when he wouldn't be seeing Kristi. Finally he invited two couples—fellow-workers and their wives. A tame enough beginning perhaps, but they stayed late and there was laughter.

Two days later there was another letter from Margaret in his box. He had it open in the elevator. She was still sending ordinary words that she expected to have answered. Little imbecile, Lars thought as he reread the letter with his coffee and leftover party-cake, where has she spent her time? Doesn't she know how frail life is? Love dies or never existed. Bodies huddle in ignominious death in elevators; what could mail photographs a day before is now a bundle to be shrieked at. Young women as much in love as you break their backs leaping from windows. Arne Svensen could have had a dozen girls by now and given one of them your red windbreaker, which you still inanely refer to as hanging in his hallway. He knew now that she was of his sort, the simple, the mocked, the used. She began to seem less pretty and somewhat older.

Her letters came intermittently after that—into the spring— always with that address in the upper corner. Sometimes he thought she'd given up and knew there was no more Arne Svensen for her. (Why did she never even suggest fear that he might have taken another woman?) Lars no longer thought seriously of return- ing the letters or sending her any word. Or at any rate not yet. He had to wait until doubt broke into her mind. He knew this was cruel and sometimes it worried him—once, in an interval between letters, he started to write her a note. But was not all life cruel? Had he not forgotten (put off) asking for February leave to take Kristi to the mountains until too late? (All the fathers of young children had wanted the school-holiday week.) Had he not, to stop Berit's yapping, signed a settlement agreement giving him every second Sunday, every third Wednesday evening and two weeks in the summer as his only time with his daughter? Had he not, through sheer ineptitude and mischance, become a thief and a pryer into other people's lies when he wanted only to love and do well to others?

Gradually he built up a picture of the woman in the distant city— a city he saw vaguely as colder, snowier and in every way harsher than Norway. And also rather open. She had a job she didn't seem to care for and that kept her very busy. (Like himself.) She had a brother and two nephews. She sometimes spent weekends with friends in Ottawa or Montreal. To his regret she gave few hard details; Arne Svensen was supposed to know all the underpinnings of her life. Mostly she wrote about things they'd done together. (If she was appealing to past love, she was doing it very skilfully. He felt he knew her and that if there were strain he'd catch it.) She'd been with Arne Svensen in a number of cities—Paris, Amsterdam, Rome, Mexico. That would have been while the old man's wife was alive. How could she afford it, Lars wondered. He had been to Paris only once—his class had splurged for their graduation journey and the Parisians had laughed and pointed at their red students' caps and ribboned willow-wands. That strange Norwegian custom of celebrating after the exams but before the results. Just as well in his case; he'd passed but not well enough to get one of the limited number of places in the medical school—and had no money to study abroad. Most of his friends had gone on to university and vanished from his life. He could hunt some of them up. And would. Soon. When...he didn't know.

With spring and the steady brightening of the evening sky, he sometimes ate dinner in town and walked for a while on Karl Johan. He became aware, as he had never been before, of how many men of his age were alone in Oslo at night. Separated or divorced. But where were the young women who matched them? Shut in some room or, if lucky, small apartment. Or back with their parents. One evening he took the little boat-tour around the Oslofjord. The night sky was a very distinct blue, the stars and the moon gold. Here again there were no Norwegian girls, only the first tourists. It seemed strange that he and all the other new bachelors were cut off from the lonely girls.

There was rain on Constitution Day but his office window gave him an excellent view of the children's parade as it surged up to the palace and he was able to lean out and catch a smile and a wave from Kristi, proud in the junior band of her school. Later, on impulse, he climbed up to the Akershus fortress and the memorial to Norwegians of the resistance who had been shot in this place. He had not seen it for years, not since his last seventeenth of May parade when he had been brought here as usual by his mother. She had—morbidly Berit said—been at pains after the war to learn the whole story; that his father, beaten at the apartment after warning his wife and child to escape, had been taken to the fortress for torture, then dragged out with others to be shot. Berit had never permitted him to tell Kristi about it or bring her here. Forget it, it's past, she always said; they did what they chose to do, let them rest. He wasn't the only one who'd come here today in the rain and a number had brought children. Father, I forgive you, he thought, speaking now not to the classic hero whom he hadn't wanted as a father but to the very young man with the smooth face like Kristi's. Or didn't he mean, Father, forgive *me*? For accepting Berit's view: Praise no one, honour no one. All simply do what they must. Not only Berit's view. He shouldn't single her out; so many reasoned in that way. But he was of another sort. He preferred to honour courage—courage beyond reason—just as he honoured love beyond reason. Quick, quick, get the boy out. And then silence under beating, under torture. He would tell Kristi now; he would even bring her here. Berit had no power over him any more.

He spent the rest of the day downtown, elated, smelling the lilacs in the rain, looking at his city as if it were quite new, and next day, among circulars and bills for himself, there was a letter from Margaret. It began like the others, small news, concern for Arne Svensen's health, it was so terrible not—Abruptly the typing broke. "My God, darling," she began on another line, "don't you know I know you're dead? Isn't there someone to tell me? I can't phone, I'm afraid to. What am I to do? Go on writing and writing on the odd chance when I know—" It ended.

"Dear Miss Margaret," Lars began very carefully, "I am sorry to have to give you these tragic news. Your dear friend Dr. Svensen ..." He sketched in the date and the circumstances, omitting the elevator. He considered this paragraph for some time, then continued, "May I say that I have been moved and impressed by your good faith. Though we are strangers, it has been of help to me at an uneasy time in my own life. I do not send your letters because I think you will not be caring to see them. But as for your jacket, if you will send me some lines, I think I can arrange to send it to you back."

He believed he'd been as kind as he could be and for a while expected an answer. He'd sunk so deeply into himself during these queer months—into himself and into her—that he'd had no sense while he wrote that he was admitting the inadmissible. The one evening it came to him. She would hate him.

She did too. All through the worst of the shock—and it was shock, against all reason she'd continued to hope—Lars figured as "that dirty little man who read my letters". But after a month or so she reread his note and caught something—a funny sort of appeal, an oddity of phrase that reminded her of Arne, that reference to her "good faith". (Had she had "good" faith? Or any other kind? Arne had hinted at marriage and she'd said "Let's talk of that next year." Because she wasn't yet used to his being free? Didn't really want the last commitment? Was afraid he felt he owed it to her? She'd never know now.) At any rate, this man knew about Arne and their love; perhaps in all the world he was the only one who did. Aside from herself. She began to be glad that someone did and even to think of writing to him and saying—well, what? She couldn't decide and finally wrote nothing though she thought of it at intervals for many months.

By now Lars had met Rondi. He had seen her several times in the laundry-room and finally dared to speak and then ask her to have coffee in the restaurant downstairs. She was thirty years old, firmly built and rather dark, not very humorous, he fancied, but with a wide and frequent smile, just the sort of sound and serious girl he felt he wanted—would want as soon as he was really free of Arne Svensen and Margaret. Kristi liked her too, which was important, since it was possible that by November, when the separation could become divorce—or, if not then, later—Kristi would be wholly his. For as he might have expected, Berit was growing tired of full-time motherhood. She had decided to be an actress and was cultivating people she thought might help her get taken on as an apprentice at one of the theatres. He was always being asked to have Kristi for an extra evening or Sunday—just this once, for some involved reason. He and his daughter were much less tense together now; she'd even found a playmate in the building and sometimes the children played in one apartment or the other while their fathers drank beer. It was more normal. He was going to take her for his summer leave to a boarding-house down the fjord. Rondi had recommended the place and was clearly hoping to be invited for weekends. And he would ask her. A little later when the time came. He had to share Margaret's mourning for a while longer. He did not know why this was so or even if it was reasonable. It was simply something he had to do.

GEORGE BOWERING

George Bowering is a prolific writer and editor, and has been a frequent contributor to Anthology *and other CBC programs. He won the Governor General's Award for poetry in the late 1960s for* Rocky Mountain Foot *and* The Gangs of Kosmos, *and the Governor General's Award for fiction in 1980 for his novel* Burning Water, *about George Vancouver's search for the Northwest Passage. One of his most interesting recent books is a critical study,* The Mask in Place: Essays on Fiction in North America. *Altogether he is the author or editor of more than forty books in many different genres. He teaches at Simon Fraser University in Vancouver.*

Bowering grew up in the Okanagan Valley in British Columbia, as the poems in "Four Jobs" indicate. The poems were broadcast on Anthology *in 1978 and are included in* West Window: The Selected Poetry of George Bowering *(General Publishing, 1982).*

Four Jobs

1. Trucking Peaches

The smell of peaches in new boxes,
seven boxes piled, I had to keep up
with the women on the sorting belt, pile
seven boxes & move them, my hand truck
leaning back over my head.

                       The women
were mothers in kerchiefs, same last names
as kids in my class, German names. They
said I was the hardest worker
in Mac & Fitz packing house & it was a shame
the way they made me run, & get rid of those
sneakers, wear boots in this place.

                             I was fifteen
but the union & Mac & Fitz agreed I was eighteen
because that was the rule. They had to give me
my 68 cents an hour.

                     I was scared shitless, Mac,
I would spill seven boxes of culled peaches
on the oiled floor & get behind hopeless & fired,
I loved the neatness, seven boxes added to
seven boxes & back of that, how it all fits
production.

                   They taught me the rules of poker too
in the lunchroom, how to guard myself from too many
65 cent bets during that one
half hour.

2. Thinning Apples

The branch goes up
when that weight comes off. I get 40 cents an hour
twisting green stems over my first knuckle,
covering the orchard floor with little green apples.

I hated working in the orchard but I liked the art
of war. Each apple was a fallen enemy
& when I got down to move my sixteen-foot ladder
my boots rolled over some & squasht some others.

So arcadian, eh? When I was thirteen
I hated it. In the morning the long grass was wet
& the air was wet & my knees & back
were sore, & in the afternoon it was a hundred degrees
& after supper I played ball or went swimming
nearly too tired to get up & go.

I ate supper at my uncle's house but I slept
in the picker's cabin, the springs were rusty
& the morning came with one hell of a bang on my door.
Imagine, me with a door.

3. Taking Pictures

The machine
munches on me.
In the air force we lined up for our pay
which came in cash. That seems now
right, it was dollars for hours, & the rest
taken care of.

                    Looking after machines, that's
what we did. I used a screwdriver to open a little
door in the aluminum wing of a cold airplane. I opened
the sixteen millimetre movie camera screwed there,
took out a cassette of negative film, & stuck in a new one.
Then I delivered it to the photo section, where I
wrote my name beside a number.

Other weeks I took the cassette from its slot beside a
number into the darkroom where I develop the film.
It was always a movie of one thing,
a target. When I delivered the film to the flight room
the flight commander learned this: how well
his student pilots could shoot machine gun bullets
at a piece of cloth.

My friends took care of jet airplanes.
I took pictures of them doing it.

If I had stayed around longer
I would have been a corporal.

4. Scrubbing the Pool

The water of the South Okanagan river system
was filled with green slime, this
became most obvious to Ron Carter & me
whose job was to clean the public swimming pool
in Lawrence, 1951.

     First it was drained
& I got there early to look for items dropt into the
water, coins felt under green slither beneath my bare
feet, a jackknife. My pants rolled up, shirt off under
the 100 degrees Fahrenheit sun, white sun from
horizon to horizon.

      First time I'd ever used the big bristles,
& a hose, to shove the slippery green stuff down to the deep,
to the drain, baring the unpainted concrete. Lawrence
was a small town for certain, outside the wire
around the pool & its two-by-four duckboard, grey dust
with a few obstinate dandelions.

       In the shell for five
hours, picking out streamers of green muck from drain
& bristles, I got sunburn & suntan, & paid
hardly anything at all. Ron Carter's father was
village commissioner so he got the job, & I got it
because he didnt want it. And my father
wanted somebody to do it, & my mother
wanted me to do something.

                    In bed for a week,
half-blind with sunstroke, I thought about how I was
an Okanagan boy & how I'd impressed everyone with
my pain,
& how I'd get out of that job.

AUDREY THOMAS

Audrey Thomas was born in Binghamton, New York, and educated at universities in the United States and Scotland. She taught for a year in England before she and her husband immigrated to Canada in 1959. They spent the years 1964–66 in Ghana. She now lives in Vancouver, writing novels and short stories and teaching at universities on the West Coast. Her fiction takes advantage of the varied places in which she has lived; novels and short stories are set in the United States, Africa, and the Gulf Islands near Vancouver, where she made her home for several years in the 1970s.

Writing about Audrey Thomas's fiction in The Oxford Companion to Canadian Literature, the critic Joan Coldwell remarks on "one of Thomas's best stories, the delicate, haunting 'Natural History'. It celebrates the love of a mother and daughter and draws together several levels of narrative into one moment of illumination." "Natural History" won an award in the CBC literary competition in 1980 and was published in Audrey Thomas's third short-story collection, Real Mothers (Talonbooks, 1981).

❖

Natural History

Something had run over her hand. Now she was wide awake and sitting up, the sleeping bag flung off, her heart pounding. What? The rat? No, don't be foolish—a mouse maybe, a vole, perhaps just the cat's tail swishing, as she came back to see if they were still persisting in this out-of-doors foolishness when there were all those comfortable beds and cushions inside. Clytie tried to get the cat to lie down at their feet, but it walked away.

"She probably thinks we're nuts," the mother said.

"Maybe she'll jump in the bathroom window and wait for us to come whining and begging to be let in."

"And she'll say, 'Well, my dears, now you know what it feels like when I want in.'"

The cat was old, but very independent, except for wanting to sleep inside at night. They often spoke for her, having endowed her with the personality of a querulous, but rather imperious, old woman.

"Maybe she'll do us the favour of catching that rat," she added.

"You *know* that she won't," the child said. "She's afraid,"

"She's not afraid; she's lazy."

But something would have to be done. No mouse could have gnawed a hole like that, right through the outside of the cottage and into the cupboard, under the sink, where the compost bucket was kept. A hole the size of a man's fist. They never saw the rat, but they heard it when they were lying in bed in the other room; and last night, it was on the roof, or rather, in the roof, directly over their heads. A determined *chewing* sound. They both woke up.

"I hope that it electrocutes itself on a wire."

"Do they really eat people?"

"No. Some of those old tales from Europe were probably based on fact. Maybe in times of famine—or when it was very cold. Maybe then. But these rats come off the fishboats; they're not starving. Rats are just big mice; there's no real biological difference." So she spoke to reassure her daughter, but nevertheless, they lay awake in the big double bed, holding hands, not liking the idea of a long, narrow, whiskered face suddenly appearing through the ceiling. Something would have to be done. She thought of rabies; she even thought of the plague. This morning, she had gone down to the store to see if they carried rat poison.

"Not any more," the storekeeper said. "We used to, but they won't let us any more. . . . Because we sell food," he added. "In case something spilled, I guess."

So, they'd have to take a trip to town and find a drugstore. Would they look at her strangely? She thought of Emma Bovary asking for arsenic. She said that she wanted to kill some rats that were keeping her awake. Cramming it into her mouth. Ugh. She would see if it were possible to get enough for only one rat. She came back up the path discouraged. She didn't want to go anywhere. She just wanted to stay here with her child and complete her recovery. Nice word that, re-cover. To cover yourself over again, something essential having been ripped away, like a deep rip in the upholstery. Then there had been the visitors to think about.

They were not sleeping outside because of the rat, but in spite of it. They were sleeping outside because of the full moon. They had talked about the moon for days. If it were fine ("And when wasn't it fine, over here, in July?" they asked each other), they would sleep out and watch the moon rise. And so, after supper, they carried out pillows and sleeping bags, a thermos of coffee and some cookies, in case they woke up early in the morning; and they made themselves a nest under the apple trees. The apples were still small and green, hardly distinguishable from the leaves. They were winter apples. There was a woven hammock that had been slung between two of the trees. She had rigged up a rope, thrown it over a stout branch and tied it, at the other end of the hammock, to a discarded wooden toy, so that one could lie in the hammock and reach up and gently rock oneself.

"The ultimate in laziness," she said. They took turns lying in the hammock, reading, the other one stretched out on an old blanket nearby.

But the moon had taken so long, so long that, first, the little girl had given a great sigh and turned over, backed up into the warmth of her mother, with her face away from the moon's rising, and slept; and then, the mother, too, slept.

But the mother was now wide awake, with the moon, high and white; and the moonlight falling over on the far side, hitting a white shed that lay beyond the house. Was it moving away from them or towards them? she wondered. Old wives' tales came back to her, about not letting the moonlight strike your face—and the memory of the blind girl that they had met that day, with her round, vacant, staring eyes. Ugh. Too many morbid thoughts.

She got up quietly and walked away a little bit to pee, squatting in the long grass. She had borrowed a scythe from a neighbour up the road, a real old-fashioned scythe, with a long wooden handle and a curved, vicious blade, and had found that, once she got the hang of it, she liked the rhythm of the thing, walking forward, moving her hips just so or the blade wouldn't cut clean, it simply hacked or flattened out the grass; but when they went to pick up the grass, they found that it was still fastened to the earth. She hadn't come around to this side yet with the scythe—perhaps tomorrow. The night was utterly still; even the owl, which they heard so often, but had never seen, was silent. And there was no breeze, except that, every so often, a ripple would pass through the firs, the alders, the pear tree and the apple trees which almost surrounded the house. It was as though the night itself were an animal, a huge dark cat which twitched and quivered from time to time in its sleep.

"I should sell this place by moonlight," she thought. "Then no one would notice the peeling paint or the cracked windowpanes or the impossible angle of the chimney."

"Describe this house," the blind girl had said, eagerly. "What does it look like?"

"It looks like a witch's house," Clytie said, without hesitation, "like something that a witch might live in." She was showing off—they had been reading Grimm's fairytales—but still, her mother was hurt.

"It's very beautiful," the blind girl's companion said. "The wall that you are leaning against is a lovely mustard-yellow and the couch that we are sitting on is purple."

"What sort of purple?"

"Very nearly the purple of that shawl you bought in Guadalajara."

So, she hadn't been blind long. Not long ago, she had seen and bought a purple shawl in a Mexican market. The girl—a young woman really—was terribly overweight and that, too, seemed recent. There was something about the way that she moved her body, or moved *in* her body, like a child all bundled up. Diabetes. Lifting the teapot, the mother's hand turned cold. The blindness, as well as the fatness, were merely signs that things inside had got out of control. What was the word? She had heard if often enough. "Stabilize." They hadn't, yet, been able to "stabilize" the disease. A seeing-eye dog, a magnificent golden Labrador, lay at the blind girl's feet. A plate of cookies was offered. They had been mixed and baked deliberately for their variety of texture: oatmeal cookies, chocolate chip, hermits. "If I'd only known", she thought. But it was interesting. Once again, the blind girl asked for visual description before she made her choice; indeed, she hardly touched the cookies at all.

Clytie watched every move, fascinated. The girl told them that she was writing poems. "Trying to get some of my anger out," she said with a little laugh. Perhaps she wanted to be asked to recite.

"We're sleeping outside tonight," Clytie said, "under the moon." The girl laughed again, the laugh too small for her large, awkward body. "Be careful not to look at a reflection of the moon in water," she said. "It's very dangerous to do that."

"Why?"

"I think that you're supposed to go mad."

Another old wives' tale.

And there was the moon now—silent, indifferent, unaware of all the myths and tales and proverbs which she had inspired! Words too, like lunatic, moony. The other day, she said to her daughter, "Stop mooning around and *do* something." As though the moon were aimless or haphazard when, in reality, she was so predictable, so orderly, that her passages could be predicted with extreme accuracy. "July 19th: Perigee moon occurs only six hours before full moon." Growing, brightening, reaching fullness; waning, dimming, beginning the whole thing over again. The old triple moon goddess, corresponding to the three phases of woman. Her little girl, Clytie, named not for the moon, but after the sunflower, was very orderly. She had drawn up a schedule at the beginning of the summer and taped it to the refrigerator door. They were going to have to work hard in the garden, yes. They were also going to have periods when each would wish to be alone, agreed; when one or the other would go out to the old shed and work on some private thing. They were going to start a study of intertidal creatures; they were going to paint the kitchen; they were going to learn the names of the constellations. There it all was, on the refrigerator door, all worked out—a calendar of orderly and edifying progression through the long summer, decorated in the corners with orange suns and purple starfish.

And there it remained, because things hadn't quite worked out like that. For one thing, it had been very hot; for another, they both seemed to have been overtaken with a kind of lethargy: the child, probably because she was growing so fast; the mother, perhaps because she was unwilling to really "come to" and think about the future.

They had worked hard during the winter, getting up at 6 a.m. and lighting fires, leaving time for a good breakfast before the yellow school bus came. And they went to bed early as well. If someone rang after 9 p.m., one or the other had to crawl out of bed in the dark to answer the phone.

She was writing a book and she worked all day while her daughter was away at school. She sat next to the wood stove, the cat asleep on a chair beside her. The simple life: it was what she craved and what she needed. On weekends, they did the wash in the old wringer-washer, shoving the clothes through the wringer with a wooden spoon; they baked bread and cookies, stacked wood, read books and listened to the radio.

"It seems so peaceful here!" the blind girl cried, as they sat in the front room, sipping tea and nibbling cookies. "It must be paradise to be here all year round."

Paradise: "a walled garden, an enclosure". Disaster: "a turning away from the stars".

The blind girl was from Los Angeles. Her companion, older,

rather stern-faced until she smiled, was the niece of one of the earliest families on the island. "She wants so much to meet you," the woman said on the phone. "I have been reading your poems to her. It would mean a great deal to her."

She did not want to meet anyone, especially anyone who had suffered, who was perhaps suffering still, but she could think of no graceful way to get out of it. It hadn't been too bad, really. She wondered and worried about her daughter's reaction, but the child seemed more interested than alarmed.

"9 a.m.: exercises, bike-riding", the schedule announced, as they sat at the kitchen table in their nightgowns, eating scones and strawberry jam. "Two hours a day, intertidal life", it called down to them from where they dozed on the rocks, the green notebook— they were still on seaweed—neglected at the bottom of the towel. They painted each other's toes and fingernails impossible colours, and waved their hands and feet in the air to dry. They timed each other to see who could stay the longest in the icy water. The yellow paint for the kitchen remained in the shed while they lay on the hammock and the blanket and read *The Wind in the Willows* out loud.

"You can't help liking Toad," Clytie said. "I know that I shouldn't like him, but I do."

Strange little creatures done up in leggings and waistcoats, thinking our kinds of thoughts and feeling our emotions. "The English were particularly good at that," she thought. "And look at me, pretending the cat will pass moral judgement on our sleeping arrangements, and feeling that, any second now, I'll see her up in a tree, grinning."

But the rat was real. The rat would have to be dealt with. "The cat takes the rat," she thought, "but maybe only in the rhyme." Sometimes, they drove down to the other end of the island to a sandy beach where the water was warmer, and they spent the afternoon and early evenings there. Last week, there had been several young women sitting on the beach with their babies and watching their older children swim. She got into a discussion with a woman that she knew slightly, whom she hadn't seen in months. The woman was very beautiful, with curly dark hair and long dancer's legs. It turned out that her husband had left her and the children to go and live with a younger woman. "I'm better now," she said, "but I spent a month thinking up ways to kill him—to kill them both. Really."

"I believe you," she said. "Last winter, I chopped kindling every day. It wasn't kindling, of course, it was hands and fingers and lips; ears, eyes, private parts. Everything chopped up small and thrown into the stove. We were as warm as toast."

"I'm glad to hear somebody else admit to such feelings," the other woman said, laughing.

"What are all those operas about, those myths, those 'crimes of passion'? We just aren't open about it in these northern climates."

"He says that he can do so much for her," the other woman said.

(And the moon up there, female, shining always by reflected light, dependent on the sun, yet so much brighter, seemingly, against the darkness of the sky; so much more mysterious, changing her shape, controlling the waters, gathering it all in her net.)

It was dark when they drove back up the island and the eyes of the deer glowed yellow-gold in the headlights. Once or twice, they saw a raccoon with eyes like emeralds.

"Why don't our eyes do that at night?"

"I don't understand it completely," she said. "It's because those animals go out at night. They have something like a mirror, maybe like your bike reflector at the back of the eye. This gives them a second chance to use whatever light there is. It hits the mirror and bounces back again. Then, what's left over shines out. 'Wasted light', I think it's called. Your grandfather taught me all that stuff. He knew all about it, but he wasn't very good at explaining it, or at least not to me. Maybe he was just tired or maybe I wasn't very good at listening. I can still remember him trying to explain about the sun and moon, one Saturday morning, when I was about your age. I don't think that I *asked* him; I think that he just wanted to explain it! He had an orange, a grapefruit, a flashlight and a pencil. He stuck a pencil through the grapefruit for the earth on its axis, but I got terribly lost. I stood on one foot and then the other, and finally, I asked if I could go out and play. I think that he was terribly hurt."

The blind girl told stories about her dog. She made everything gay and light and witty. Once, she and another blind friend had taken their dogs into a posh Los Angeles restaurant. "It's against the law to keep us out," she explained. It was the friend's birthday, so they saved up their money to go out together and celebrate. The waiter was very helpful and they ordered a fancy meal. Their dogs lay quiet and well-behaved beneath the table. Everybody felt good.

"Then, Samson sort of sat up—I could feel him. He gave a sigh and did a huge shit, right by my chair. It was *so* awful. We could hear the people who were nearest to us, saying, 'Well, *really*,' and similar things. The smell was very powerful and we got hysterical. We were laughing our heads off at the whole idea. We could sort of 'feel' the maître d' hovering nearby, uncertain whether or not to kick these gross blind people out and maybe face some sort of lawsuit, or lose all his patrons; or just try to ignore the whole thing, pick up the poop and carry on."

"What happened?" At the mention of his name, the dog sat up, wagging his tail, as though he, too, were enjoying the story.

"Well, I carefully lowered my big, beautiful, starched dinner napkin, over where I thought the pile was—I didn't actually want to get my fingers in it—and then I called out: '*Waiter, waiter*. I'm afraid my dog has had a little accident.'"

"But we never went back there," she added when they stopped laughing. "Never."

"I would not have offered cookies," she thought, "if I had known. I would not have *tempted* her, especially with homemade cookies, offered by the young girl who had home-made them." The man who tried to teach her about the motions of the sun and moon and earth on its axis had been a diabetic too, or had become one, only much later in life than their visitor. He could not give up all the sweet rich foods that he loved. He was dead now; he did not even know that she had a child. "Just this once," he used to say, as he put sugar on his grapefruit, or ordered a dish of chocolate ice-cream. And her mother, joining in, would say, "Oh, it won't hurt him, just this once." He had been quite short-sighted and the thing that made her realize how dead he was, was, after the funeral, finding his bifocals in a drawer. How many cookies had the blind girl eaten? She couldn't remember.

"I don't really feel lonely any more," she said to her friend on the beach. "I used to. I used to think that I'd die from loneliness, as if it were a disease. I suppose that I'll want to be with someone again, but right now, I'm content. Only, some days—when the fucking clothesline breaks or I'm down to the wet wood, things like that—I wish that there were someone around. But then, I ask myself, 'Is it a husband that I want or a hired hand'?"

"A hired hand might be useful for other things as well."

"Or a hired finger." They giggled.

(He would have dealt with this rat, for instance. He would have got rid of it quick.)

One night, the cat caught a mouse and started munching it in the darkness of the room where she and Clytie were sleeping.

"*Really*," she said, waking up and recognizing what was going on.

And Clytie, laughing, got up in her long white nightdress and threw the cat outside.

She wasn't the least afraid of that. But she was terrified to be alone in the dark, as her mother had been terrified when she was a child, as perhaps all children were terrified of the dark. Which is why she sat here, now, wide awake and thoughtful, her half of the sleeping bag over her knees, rather than inside the house, sipping a cup of tea and reading until she became sleepy again.

They had done away with mousetraps because they couldn't stand that awful, final "click".

"Ugh," the child said, crawling back in bed, "that crunching sound was really *disgusting*." And they both began to laugh.

"Shall we make her a mouse pie the next time she does that?"

"Would you? Would you really?"

"Why not?"

"It might smell terrible."

"Would you really make a mouse pie with a crust, like in *The Pie and the Pattypan*?"

"Oh God, I don't know. . . .Probably not."

They caught a rock cod near the government wharf and when they cleaned it and removed the stomach, there were three small crabs inside.

"I suppose that they have some sort of acid in their stomachs which dissolves the shell," she said.

"I guess everything just goes around eating everything else," her child said.

"Sometimes it seems that way."

The blind girl turned her head towards whomever was speaking; she turned towards the sound. The sunflower, Clytie, following her beloved Apollo as he crossed the sky. The moon, shining always with reflected light.

"Where are all the strong men," the woman on the beach said, "now that there are all these strong women?"

("I'm getting awfully symbolic out here, wide awake beneath the moon." The absolute trust of her sleeping child moved her almost to tears. She would sit here all night, if necessary; it didn't matter.)

"I can't stay on this island forever," she thought. "I will end up like an old witch in a witch's cottage. I've got to give my life some serious attention. It's all very well to sit around reading fairytales and making a game of everything." She glanced at her daughter's long hair which was spread out on the pillow beside her. "*She'll* change; maybe she'll change first. She'll want more than this." Her namesake, turned into a sunflower, gazing blindly towards the sun. The moon (female), shining always by his light.

("Let her be strong," she thought. "Let her be strong and yet still loving." A few years ago, in the city, she had come home from school and announced, at dinner, that a policeman had come to the school and given a talk about "strangers". Her mother and father glanced quickly at one another. A little girl, her lunchbox beside her, had been found dead in a ditch.

"And what are strangers?" asked her father gently, curious as to what she had been told, yet wanting to keep the story light.

The child's reply was very serious.

"Strangers are usually men.")

"Dis-aster", they read in the dictionary: "a falling away from the stars". "Paradise", from the Persian: "a walled garden". "*Lunaticus*" f. L., "affected by the moon". And who had first made *that* connection? Galileo. He built this "optik glasse" and discovered that the moon (female, shining always with reflected light) was not the "luminous orb" of the poets, but rather, full of "vast protuberances, deep chasms and sinuosities".

Later, in England, men looked at a flea through a microscope and saw "the devil shut up in a glasse". Mankind was always wanting more, wanting to make far things nearer, small things larger; to know and understand it all. When the Americans stepped on the moon, one of her friends had written a long mock-heroic poem called "The Rape of Cynthia".

The trick was, of course, to try and get the right distance on everything; to stand in just the right relationship to it all. But how? Would her daughter be any better at in than she was? Another image came to mind, out of her childhood, a stereopticon belonging to her grandfather. She would sit with it, on a Sunday afternoon, sliding the crossbar up and down, until suddenly, "click", the two photographs taken at slightly different angles (St. Mark's, the Tower of London, Notre Dame) would become one picture, which would take on depth and a wonderful illusion of solidity. *That* was the trick. To slide it all—moon, blind girl, rat, the apple tree, her father's fingers tilting the pencil, her own solitude, the cat, the eyes of the deer, her daughter, this still moment, back/forth, back/forth, back/forth, until "click",

until "click",

until "click"—

there it was: wholeness, harmony, radiance; all of it making a wonderful kind of sense, as she sat there under the apple tree, beneath the moon.

And then, suddenly, because she *did* see, if only for an instant, she bent down and she shielded the child's body as the moonlight, finally, reached them.

"What amazes me," Clytie said, just before she turned over and went to sleep, "is that we're just part of a system. We're all just floating around."

NORTHROP FRYE

A CONVERSATION WITH ROBERT FULFORD

The conversation between Robert Fulford and Northrop Frye was a joint venture by Anthology *and the literary annual* Aurora, *edited by Morris Wolfe and published by Doubleday Canada. The conversation was broadcast on* Anthology *in the fall of 1980 and published at about the same time in the third issue of* Aurora, *which unfortunately also brought to an end that interesting literary experiment.*

Robert Fulford has been the editor of Saturday Night *since 1968; he writes a weekly column for the* Toronto Star *and appears often on radio and television. While Northrop Frye is a literary critic of international influence and reputation, he has never neglected the literature of his own country. The* Bush Garden: Essays on the Canadian Imagination *is Frye's major work about Canadian writing.*

❖

From Nationalism to Regionalism: The Maturing of Canadian Culture

FULFORD: Culture in Canada in the 1970s expanded enormously in numbers, in everything from the number of books of poetry published to the number of dancers employed. But as the decade ended there was a sense of—maybe not despair, but certainly disappointment that somehow things hadn't worked out as everyone had hoped or expected. Did you get that feeling?

FRYE: I'm not so sure. I think there are other factors such as the growing recognition of Canadian literature outside Canada, and a growing response to it which I find almost miraculous. I don't understand what people on the continent of Europe get out of Canadian literature, but they certainly get something out of it, and it registers as a kind of unified statement to them. With us it's the ordinary entropy which seems to set in with almost any cultural movement after a few years. Perhaps we'll be refreshed by seeing our mirror images coming back to us from other countries.

FULFORD: When I read about the culture of various periods, usually in Europe but to some extent in America, I see again and again the well-to-do playing a part—the person, say, who founds a dance company with her father's millions. Is there something that keeps Canadian private money from being interested in the arts? You don't have in this country the families—one thinks of the Guggenheims or the Rockefellers—who in the United States pour in millions of dollars. One thinks of patrons of the arts throughout European history. Nothing like that seems to happen here.

FRYE: No, it doesn't happen. I think we are basically a country of deficit financing, and we tend to look to government agencies to subsidize culture just as we look to government agencies to set up a broadcasting commission or a national railway or a National Film Board. Consequently, private business seems to feel that's something they pay taxes for anyway and don't need to support further. I think a peculiar feature of Canadian cultural life is its dependence on government assistance.

FULFORD: Peculiar for a democracy anyway. In a democracy it's unusual to find the government as the mainstay, without a powerful equivalent in the private sector. It seems to me, though, that in the period we're talking about, the 1970s, that government has not been as much help as it might have been, even though the federal government spent a lot more money than ever before. The government really hasn't demonstrated strong leadership. I wonder if it would have been different if Pierre Trudeau had been as interested in the development of Canadian culture as he was in renewed federalism and the constitution.

FRYE: I have a notion that the government's attitude to culture should be a fairly relaxed one. It's more a matter of trying to let the cultural imagery of the country emerge, than providing leadership for it. I'm not just sure where government leadership would take it. I think that as a culture matures, it becomes more regional anyway. And whatever a culture does, if it's worth doing, there's going to be a strongly unpredictable element in it. I think the best and wisest government policy is to allow for a certain leeway, to allow for the spontaneity of cultural expression. In the natural course of events the real initiative comes from the creative people themselves. They know what they want to do, and they can go to a foundation, whether it's a government one or a private one as in the States, and say, "Look, I've got a wonderful idea", and the foundation's job is to evaluate the idea and to respond accordingly.

FULFORD: But there *are* things that governments can do. If we talk about the Canada Council, the government by an act of will created that foundation. And then it determined its size. The Canada Council is now—I don't know what—ten times the size it was when it was founded. But it could be fifty times that size. Or it could be half the size. Those are key government decisions made in cabinet and caucus and so on. They may not determine the quality of the cultural life of the country but they determine whether there will *be* one. That is, by saying, "All right, we'll have a Canada Council in 1990 that's five times the size of the present one", they would call into being twenty more dance companies or three opera companies, or a lot more publishing houses, or something like that. So there is a sense in which they *are* crucially involved at least in a quantitative sense.

FRYE: They're involved in the quantitative sense but there's a fine line, I think, between *laissez-faire*, saying the culture can look after itself, which in our case would mean that culture would still be at a pretty undeveloped state, and assuming leadership, actually providing the cultural ideas.

FULFORD: It seems to me in looking at the 1970s that one of the most striking features is the diminishing role of some of our major cultural institutions. Even though some of them have grown larger, they seem less visible. Some of them ended the 1970s less important than they began them. I'm thinking of the National Film Board, which at times seems to vanish from sight; of the Canada Council, which seems dispirited and defensive even though it has grown considerably. I'm thinking of the National Gallery, which, to anyone who goes in to see their exhibitions, seems to be a shambles. Major cultural institutions to which we looked for some kind of leadership, or coherence, some way of making our culture accessible and understandable— they seem to be slipping into the background.

FRYE: There are several processes at work there. One is that anyone handling so expensive a medium as television or film tends to get mired in real estate, bureaucracy and vested interest. I hesitate to draw the inference that there is a connection between limited funds and liveliness of intellect, but it *is* true that when these things started (the National Film Board, CBC television) there was a feeling, not merely of starting something new, but of defining oneself over again to society. I think culture always has to have a feeling of *cult* about it. And again I hesitate to say that complete public tolerance of, say, the art of painting would tend to make painting rather decorative—that is, it would become simply a function of society and not the voice of a creative impulse that is stirring and prodding the society. I think that those things have set in in many respects. The golden days of the National Film Board had a lot to do with its defining itself as an entity in the Grierson days. And similarly with the CBC, where the level in radio, I think, is much higher than the level in television simply because it is more of a minority medium.

FULFORD: What you're suggesting is that one has to have some kind of outsider status in order to come to life. You can't be totally accepted and still remain culturally alive.

FRYE: I think the question of defining oneself as a presence over or against a society is pretty essential for the creative life. I think that it's been an immense advantage to the writers and creative people in Quebec to feel that they were fighting for a beleaguered and threatened language. And I think that separatism is a very unattractive combination of a progressive cultural movement and a regressive political one—and that the cultural side is the *genuine* part of it.

FULFORD: It seems to me that in the 1970s regionalism became the dominating force in the culture. Maybe it was always so, and became a lot more visible in the 1970s.

FRYE: Regionalism is an inevitable part of the maturing of the culture of a society like ours. I think that in this "instant world of communications", as it's called, there is a kind of uniform international way of seeing and thinking which is derived from the fact that everybody is involved in the same technology. Regional developments are a way of escaping from that, developing something more creative. If you want to learn about *American* life from its literature, for example, you learn about it inferentially from what Faulkner tells you about Mississippi and what others tell you about New England or the Middle West. That is becoming increasingly true of Canada, where the conception of Canada doesn't really make all that much sense. "Canada" is a *political* entity; the cultural counterpart that we call "Canada" is really a federation not of provinces but of regions and communities.

FULFORD: To me it was very striking that in the 1970s one began to be able to read poetry and guess what region the poet was from without reading the poet's biography. I don't think that was true ten or fifteen years before.

FRYE: It's an inevitable part of the maturing of the culture. One area after another becomes culturally articulate through its writers. If you want to know about Canada from its culture, look to see what Jack Hodgins has to say about Vancouver Island, or James Reaney or Robertson Davies about southwestern Ontario, or Roger Lemelin about Quebec. If you add up the cultural communities you get a sense of the vitality and variety of Canadian culture.

FULFORD: Can you see a time when there'll be *national* cultural figures? In my lifetime the only people who have done it have been the Group of Seven. They created a kind of art that has strong adherents in every region, and in both language groups.

FRYE: The Group of Seven were really pre-Canadian in the sense that they were imaginative explorers. Their literary counterpart would not be our established writers so much as people like David Thompson and Samuel Hearne. They were the end of a long period of exploratory and documentary painting which plunged into the country in the wake of the voyageur. I think the country we know as Canada will, in the foreseeable future, be a federation of regions culturally, rather than a single nation. I think cultural nationalism gets confused about its units and tends to introduce unreal forms of casuistry, that is, what is truly Canadian and so on. The question can be answered more precisely in different terms.

FULFORD: When I've lectured in a different part of the country from the one I live in, Toronto, and when some element of what I regard as cultural nationalism comes into what I'm saying, there's always an objection. I remember a painter in Halifax telling me that my point of view was that of Ontario politics, not Canadian nationalism at all. It had nothing to do with Halifax, he said.

FRYE: I can understand that reaction very well. I was brought up in the Maritimes myself. I think it's been of an immense benefit to Canada first that it went from a pre-national phase to a post-national phase without ever quite becoming a nation, and second that it never tried to be homogeneous, a melting pot. It always let ethnic groups have their own head, culturally speaking, and I think that is of tremendous benefit to the variety of our culture. To some extent the melting pot, the homogeneity, occurs anyway in response to certain social conditions, and it happens all the better if it isn't too much forced from the outside. The process takes longer. There are many elements in Canadian life—I'm thinking of the Ukrainians and the Icelandics, of the Mennonites in the prairies—they have all made a distinctive appearance in our literature and our painting which, I think, is all to the good. Of course, I see it as a minority movement.

FULFORD: But television is the most pervasive conveyor of culture and, many people believe, the most important one. Yet in this period, despite what we've said about regionalism, and in a period which has been characterized as nationalistic, Canadians have watched less and less *Canadian* television and more and more American television. Do you think this is, in any significant way, the fault of the government, or of the CRTC, of which you were a member? Or is it simply a function of North Americanism? Was it inevitable, no matter what we did?

FRYE: I think it was inevitable. I joined the CRTC in 1968, when the new Broadcasting Act made a good deal of sense. And then what happened was the practically autonomous, it seemed, development, through microwave and cable satellite and pay TV, of new technology that tends to follow the centralizing political and economic rhythms rather than the decentralizing cultural ones. And every new medium seems to have to recapitulate a history from a very archaic phase to a very sophisticated one. I think in radio and film we're a long way now from Amos and Andy and the Keystone Cops. Television is still pretty formulaic. But mass culture is just *that*—it's what the vast majority of people want. If we speak of Canada being flooded with American programs, we find that the Canadian viewer is a fish, not somebody who wants to get into a Canadian ark, floating on top.

FULFORD: What happened was that the technology had control of the CRTC, rather than the CRTC having control of the technology.

FRYE: The technology took the bit in its teeth, and there wasn't much that any government regulatory agency could do about it.

FULFORD: Cable made all this American programming available, the people gobbled it up, and nothing you could have done would have changed that.

FRYE: I don't think that anything could really have changed that.

But there will be other technological developments in Canada that will again regionalize things, and bring smaller communities into focus.

FULFORD: Then you see the development of a more sophisticated form of television which will encourage a more sophisticated form of culture, namely regionalism.

FRYE: I think it's inevitable that as any medium matures it tends to become more directly an expression of human beings, rather than an expression of mass formulae.

FULFORD: Certainly we can see that with phonograph records. There was a period when there were about four record companies in North America, and they put out a few records every week, and everyone in North America was expected to know about those records and hear them. Then, as the industry became more sophisticated with the development of the LP and cheaper means of pressing, the process became much more sophisticated. In that case, regionalism could express itself through phonograph records. Indeed very sophisticated kinds of culture can express themselves through that medium, while at the same time the million-seller, the gold record and so on reach the mass market. The technology has made possible hundreds of other forms of expression. But I'm interested in pursuing your idea that as culture becomes more sophisticated it also becomes more local or regional. It seems to me that's the opposite of many people's view of culture. Those people see big cities and the development of communication as making it possible to centralize culture.

FRYE: I see increasing regionalism as a way of the creative mind escaping from a centralizing uniformity. I was in New Zealand recently, and in Guyana for a week, and I looked into the literature of New Zealand and of the Caribbean, and I noticed intense regionalism alongside certain ways of handling time and space and characterization which reminded me strikingly of what I've seen in Canadian as well as British and American literature. I think we can take the centralizing aspect of contemporary culture for granted. But it's at that point that the growth towards more and more regionalism begins. If you get on a jet plane, you can't expect a different culture in the place where the plane lands, but you will find different people, and the creative people will be aware of the differences.

FULFORD: In other words, if you go to Guyana you may find as you glance around, first of all that everyone watches American television, or American films, but then you will also find an intense local expression.

FRYE: Yes. Although Guyana is not really a clear example, because they don't get American television. But if they did, it would be the same thing as you have here: the mass response is for the mass culture, but within that, little creative pockets form.

FULFORD: I saw an Australian film last year, *Newsfront*, about people working in newsreels in Melbourne—and it was astoundingly like Toronto. People I've known for twenty years were in that film, except they were speaking with an Australian accent and had different faces. They were the same people with the same attitudes and the same views and the same resentment of Los Angeles and the same hope—to create something uniquely their own. That feeling of resistance towards a distant metropolis which is really in control of mass culture came through very strongly.

FRYE: Yes, that's part of the general uniformity of attitude, I think.

FULFORD: A curious thing has happened in a field which I take a special interest in, and that's making films for theatrical distribution. It seems to me that Canada has actually stepped back from the position it held, very shakily, a decade ago, before the Canadian Film Development Corporation came along. The Quebec films of the 1960s were quite interesting, and they had audiences, and I think they'll always be looked at as something important about that period. And there were a few films from English Canada around that period which were interesting too. But we had nothing then that most people would call a film industry. Now we have, but we've gone backwards, because we're not making *Canadian* movies any more. In a curious way the government has helped to set up an imitation Hollywood in Canada. We're making movies that almost no one, even the producers, would claim have anything to do with Canada. Work has been provided for some people. That's about all that can be said for it.

FRYE: Well, I think there's a powerful undertow in both film and television which follows the centralizing political and economic rhythms of the country rather than the decentralizing cultural rhythms. Certainly that undertow has been very evident in both film and television in Canada. The CRTC Canadian content regulations look rather unreal now. And yet I think that the tendency which is built into the technology and into the quality of response has to work itself out, and one shouldn't be too discouraged by finding that these media from time to time relapse into commercial formulas and mass productivity.

FULFORD: In a curious way, what has happened in the Canadian film industry is that it's become an inferior Hollywood. It hasn't developed that edge of creativity which you see in a number of current American filmmakers such as Coppola and Altman. Nothing of that kind has happened in the Canadian context. It's all been imitative, and imitating something that someone saw four years ago.

FRYE: A great many people make the same remark about Canadian television. They would say that it is bad American television and that the best American television is far better.

FULFORD: The matter of films and television opens up the larger question of the Americanization of Canada. Some people believe that only a tiny number of Canadians are touched by anything that could be called Canadian culture. And almost everyone in the country has now been submerged by American culture.

FRYE: The phenomenon that we call mass culture is uniform in the United States and English Canada. I'm not greatly worried about what is called the Americanization of Canada. What people mean when they speak of Americanization has been just as lethal to American culture as it has been to Canadian culture. It's a kind of levelling down which I think every concerned citizen of democracy should fight, whether he is a Canadian or an American.

FULFORD: And yet there is a choice between American and Canadian culture in some areas. For instance, I remember a friend who was teaching in a community college in southwestern Ontario when the War Measures Act was brought in, who discovered that most of what his students knew about the War Measures Act they knew from what Walter Cronkite told them. The fact is that Walter Cronkite, and those broadcasts, are an expression of America, even though it may be a levelled America. And so are movies. Movies can be good or bad expressions of America. They can be levelling, or they can be defining, but they *are* America. And they leave out the reality of Canada.

FRYE: I think that to the extent that they become *genuine* American cultural products, they tend more and more to speak for a smaller community than the United States of America. While Faulkner is not a part of American *mass* culture, he is a very articulate expression of American culture. But the American part is an inference from what he tells you about his corner of America.

FULFORD: Paradoxically, although I'm as worried as anyone about the phenomena we've been discussing, the curious thing is that the Canadians I know are much more Canadian today than they were twenty-five years ago. By Canadian I mean sophisticated to some extent about the different parts of Canada, interested and so on. For instance, my daughter's friends and the students I encounter when I go out to teach, and the young people who come into my office—they know vastly more about Newfoundland, or Alberta, or Quebec than I did when I was eighteen or twenty or twenty-five in Toronto. Something has happened, and I think it's television. Television has worked for a lot of these people.

FRYE: Television does have a profoundly civilizing aspect in that it compels people to look like people. I think of what an abstract notion I had of Eskimos when I was a student at school, or even college, and how that simply disappeared as soon as one began seeing them on television.

FULFORD: You have to accept René Lévesque as a human being when you see him three times a week on the eleven o'clock news.

FRYE: You have to start whittling away your stereotypes.

FULFORD: When the 1970s began we had a crisis in the publishing business which led to a great deal of government activity. Ryerson Press was purchased by an American firm, McGraw-Hill. The Ontario government appointed a Royal Commission. The Canada Council threw itself into a frenzy of activity. The Secretary of State made various moves. And a publishing community of a kind was created. What's been the result of that? Has it affected you? Has it changed what you're reading in any way?

FRYE: I'm not sure that it has, really. The publishing and selling of books is an economic enterprise; it follows economic rhythms, rather than strictly cultural ones. It didn't worry me too much that certain publishers in Canada were British, like Macmillan and Oxford, because they were working very hard and conscientiously to produce Canadian books. I regret the kind of nationalism that defines a Canadian publisher in artificial terms. A certain amount of takeover is almost inevitable, given the economic conditions. Canadian authors in the meantime seem to continue to get published. And it doesn't worry me too much if a roomful of Canadian schoolchildren is asked who the Prime Minister of Canada is and say Jimmy Carter. What interests me is that Jimmy Carter is reading Peggy Atwood. The growth of

Canada as a distinctive presence in the world scene is something that's also going on.

FULFORD: The idea that in Italy and elsewhere there are courses in Canadian literature would have seemed outlandish ten or fifteen years ago. How do you explain that? Is Canada becoming exotic in some way?

FRYE: It's partly that, but I think too it's the maturing of a culture. An immature culture imports its culture. So long as Canada was a colony, the works of British and American literature were brought out to the boondocks and people tried to imitate them. But as a culture matures, it becomes a native manufacture, and eventually it's an export. Canada is now producing a literature which has an imaginative integrity to other countries. I was talking with a professor at the University of Bordeaux who spoke eloquently about Canadian literature as the expression of a people finding its own voice. I assumed he meant French-Canadian literature, but he didn't. He meant English-Canadian writers like Margaret Laurence and Timothy Findley and Jack Hodgins—writers working within a region.

BILL
SCHERMBRUCKER

"Aga Dawn", which might best be described as a fictional memoir, won an award in the memoirs section of the CBC literary competition for 1980. Its author, Bill Schermbrucker, grew up in Kenya and came to Canada in the 1960s. He teaches English at Capilano College, a community college in North Vancouver. "Aga Dawn" was published in Mr. Schermbrucker's first book, Chameleon and Other Stories *(Talon Books, 1983).*

✦

Aga Dawn

All his life, my father got up at the crack of dawn, without an alarm clock. We lived almost on the equator, so dawn was regular at about 5:45, and didn't vary more than fifteen or twenty minutes throughout the year. I suppose he must have slept in at times, but if so I can't remember them. As a rule, I'd wake up and hear him moving about in his slippers. Or I'd sense that he had already been in the kitchen, which was close to my room. Perhaps it was the slight bang he made, putting the kettle onto the Aga Cooker, that would wake me.

He had the Aga specially installed. The workmen had to break down and rebuild the kitchen wall to get it in. Before that, we had an electric stove; and before that, an old Dover wood stove, on cast iron legs, that filled the kitchen with smoke. "It's darned nigh impossible to make a cup of tea around here!" my father complained. So, for his birthday, my brother and I pooled our pocket money and bought him a Tea-Cal. This machine consisted of a sealed electric kettle, like a small pressure cooker, on a tilting base, with a silver tube that came out of the lid and down the side to the teapot. On the other end of the base was a lamp and a clock. It worked like a simple alarm. In preparation for your convenient, modern awakening, you filled the kettle, set the clock, and positioned the tea tray on your bedside table in such a way that the pot, with tea-leaves already measured into it, sat with its lid off, right under the silver tube. At the set time, the kettle would switch on, and, when it boiled, the steam pressure would blow the boiling water through the tube and into the teapot. As the last ounce emptied, the base on which the empty kettle sat would tilt up, while the lamp and clock went down. This see-saw movement switched off the kettle, tripped the alarm and switched on the light, so the sleeper would wake suddenly to a steaming pot of tea, and light to pour it by. We thought it was wonderful! We rushed to my father's bedroom on his birthday and, after he tore open the package, we both jabbered explanations at the same time.

He thought it was wonderful too. "Abso-lutely splendid!" He used it sometimes, to humour us. What he appreciated was the personal touch: that we had recognized his early morning habits and chosen a suitable gift. "Suitable", that is, as a symbol, for, with us, it was always the thought that counted. As for making tea, well, he was not the kind of man (we realized later) to rely on some new-fangled American gadget—especially not one bringing water and electricity together right beside the bed. He had his own standards of safety, and preferred to do things his own way.

For early morning tea, his own way consisted of junking the electric stove ("it never worked properly") and installing in its place the gigantic, coal-burning Aga.

The Aga ran on anthracite, imported from Wales. It had an oven big enough to accommodate a couple of large turkeys and, on the top, there were two hotplates of solid cast iron, each almost three feet in diameter, with heavy, shining covers. At night, the cook would narrow the flues, give one precise pull-push to the ash dispenser, hidden behind a small enamelled door, add a handful of coal and then gently lower the covers onto their asbestos brims around the hotplates. This kept the heat in, and the stove burning till morning. It was never allowed to go out. The Aga dominated our kitchen, and was not referred to in English as a "stove", but "The Aga Cooker". In my mind, our house began to acquire some odd connection with diamonds, horse races and Paris, from the homophones, "Aga Cooker/Aga Khan".

During the War, my mother had worked as a nurse in the Aga Khan clinic in Pumwani. A framed citation for service hung in our passageway, just beyond where guests would turn to go to the bathroom. I was always conscious of that hanging frame, but its location puzzled me. I could understand why my father had the citation framed, out of the usual family loyalty which was a firm priority. And I could understand his putting it down at the bathroom end of the passage, so as not to advertise our connection with "Indians"—even though they were "Aga Khan Indians", which, for some reason, were considered more acceptable. But I didn't understand why he risked the public exposure at all. Why not put it right in his bedroom, where there was *no* chance of a stray guest happening to see it? One day, when I was alone in the house and snooping through my parents' clothing drawers, I found some tickets for the Aga Khan Sweepstake among my father's socks. I decided to accost him.

"Father," I said innocently over soup, "who exactly *is* the Aga Khan?"

"Oh..." His face took on that sombre half-frown which was as typical of him after a day of legal wrangles as his bright beams were in the early morning. "He's a rather *hoi polloi* type, who nevertheless manages to do a lot of good in the world."

These were precise and antithetical terms. I understood at once why the citation hung where it did, in middle ground between acceptance and disapproval. In my father's vocabulary, there were three ranks of moral excellence. The rare ones "did a lot of good in the world", and they were the top bananas. Then came "salt of the earth". Then "sound as a rock".

The "salt of the earth" were generally poor people who persevered through incredible difficulties with a smile. They "made a go of it", even though they were "worse off than we are". The example they set was inspiring, so that my father easily forgave them for sins incurred in "making a go". (A borrowed blanket that never came back after the War; a sworn statement that turned out to be "a white lie".)

Quite a few people were "sound as a rock". They were fine enough, but not inspiring: certain unswayable judges, or those particular in-laws to whom my father would send off a hefty loan, "without a moment's qualm". Also, some newspapers, the old *Sunday Post*, for instance ("Sound as a rock!" I can hear him still), whereas the lively new *Daily Nation* never made it past being "a bit of a nonsense" in my father's eyes.

But the Aga Khan "did a lot of good in the world". That put him right up there with the Salvation Army (for whom my parents and my godparents would always stop the car and offer a ride), and my

blind physiotherapist uncle. They served people with a generosity
father always wished he had, and knew he didn't. Secretly, he was
ashamed of the fact that, for all the appearance he gave of doing
good, it wasn't finally "in the world" that he did it. He wrote
letters and sent cheques. He was a little in awe of my mother, who
could toil all day in the overcrowded clinic amid pain and disease.
In praising the Aga Khan, my father's eyes looked down, even as his
eyebrows went up, admitting to himself, perhaps, as he had always
known, that in the final judgement his own contribution to the
universe would be ranked a step or two lower than the top.

For all his eminence though, the Aga Khan was also "a *hoi polloi*"
type to father: shallow and flashy; a gambler with the odds;
someone who set style above common sense, who dressed flamboy-
antly and spoke with a hot potato in his mouth. (Years later, with
freshman intensity, I pressed correction on him: "It means *common-
ers*, father, the very *opposite* of aristocracy, the *polloi*, you see, the *city
crowd*!" and he grunted, mistrustful. But I noticed after that he used
the term "hoity-toity" instead.)

So anyway, when the Aga Cooker came, I stood breathless as they
sledged out the stone wall with a mighty hammer. Its huge, new
presence in the house filled me with a kind of guilty excitement. As
a stove, it was extremely efficient, and I heard father prove over and
over again that it was cheaper in the long run to burn imported
anthracite than firewood cut on his own property. But there was
something about the heaviness of those enormous shiny covers—
the hugeness of such a stove against the apparent slightness of early
morning tea—that gave me a thrill. With the coming of the Aga,
something had happened in our house. My father—a man of
ultimate discretion, who even, in later life, nagged and nagged at
you to go down to the police station and fill out an accident report
if you nudged a bumper parking; a man who would turn around
and drive back three miles to return a ballpoint pen accidentally
carried away from a restaurant; a man of such self-effacing respecta-
bility that, for months, he went through agony each morning
opening the newspaper after my brother had had his camera
confiscated by British Customs, his heart doing double time while
he scanned the pages for the big black headlines: MIS-DECLARA-
TION BY KENYAN or (God *help* us!) LAWYER'S SON
CHARGED—this man, had lowered his defences enough to let
this blatant oddity, the Aga, into his house. It really stirred my
imagination. I wondered at first if he had taken it as a legal fee. It

didn't seem possible that he had done such a thing for his own gratification.

By morning, the chrome spring handles of the Aga's covers were too hot to touch, but once you got a cloth onto one, and swung the heavy lid back onto its stop, a blast of heat came off that surface such as no other stove could give. You put the kettle on, and immediately the water would begin singing up to a boil. And the Aga had its own special kettle, with a thick, machined base, about eighteen inches across, which narrowed sharply towards the top, and held two quarts of water. It was this that must have clinched the sale. I can picture my father standing there, wearing his barrister's scepticism balanced against fair-mindedness, holding the stopwatch the salesman has handed him; he clicks *on* to the salesman's "Now!" and the kettle goes onto the plate. He clicks *off* as the jet of steam shoots from the spout. "Hmmph! Forty-one seconds."

That original occasion is easy to picture, from the many times I followed, as he led a guest to the kitchen after dessert, to demonstrate. The servants, of course, were happy as hell. Not only did Bwana get his own tea in the morning, which meant the cook could sleep in till seven, but, when guests came to dinner, there was always a good chance of quitting early. As the last tray was being cleared off the table, Bwana would raise his eyes and instruct, in that simplification of ki-Swahili known as ki-Settler: "*Wewe na wesa kwenda sasa, Kakui. Mombia 'Mpishi kufunga jiko 'msuri!*" ("You can go now, Kakui. Tell Cook to close the stove properly.") There was no more chopping of wood, or carrying it in. And, so complete was the combustion of the Welsh steam coal that the ashes amounted to one small metal drawerful a month. And, oh, I'm sure my father was conscious of all these peripheral advantages of the Aga, but the main one was simple: he could wake up in the morning, slide feet into slippers, tie the sash of his beige, woollen, Whiteaway-Laidlaw dressing gown as he strode down the parquet-floored passage to the hot kitchen, and, there, fill the kettle, lift the heavy lid back, set it on, turn around and lay a tray, turn around and pour!

It was something that *worked*, by God, in a world increasingly filled with gadgets and junk; a world of growing political noise and unrest; a world in which Americans, with their sickening nasal parody of proper speech, and their long short pants that clung to the thigh like a corset, were beginning to step out of the movies in which they belonged, and appear on the streets and in the offices of Nairobi, talking not now about dead lions and elephants, but about mineral *po*tential, biladeral in*eesh*adives, and the dangers of cawmunism. The street names were changing. Statues vanished.

How my father hated change. How he loved the dawn. I think the rising of the sun and his Aga Cooker were the last constants left for him in the world. And yet, he would go out in his dressing gown in the morning dew, to prune the coffee, read the rain gauge and write down the points in his rain record book, as though, in some way, he still believed in the future that he hated to see coming. "It will see out my time," he used to say, meaning the country.

Our house had nose-deep foundations of solid blue stone. That is, we dug till my father could stand in the trench and his nose came to ground level—so that one day a second storey could be added on, with a clear view over the coffee to The Mountain, Mt. Kenya, a hundred miles away. This was my mother's idea, like most of the plans to do with the house. She wanted the house in the coffee, not under the gum trees, and facing east-northeast, straight to The Mountain. She wanted rose trellises, bougainvillea, beds of poppies, zinnias and Michaelmas daisies, with a Swazi grass lawn and a finer Paspalum lawn under the bedroom windows. Parquet flooring in the main wing of the house, red cement in the kitchen wing, and a walled yard, so that the washing would hang safe from thieves. Although she was content with district water for washing, and resigned herself to the two squat tanks of it on the cement platform above the yard wall, ensuring the supply against water cuts, for drinking, for washing woollens, she demanded rain water. Since the rains came only in April, May and November, this meant a huge storage tank, 5,000 gallons, and periodic sweeping of the roof. When my father told her that he didn't want servants walking around up there, causing leaks in the corrugated iron, she said that she would sweep the roof herself.

Unfortunately, she died early. She never lived in the house, except for a few bedridden months between hospitals. I took a snapshot of her in a bush hat, squatting near some Barberton daisies, smiling. But my only real memory of her in the house is when she was lying in bed, crying from the pain of her illness. It would not be easy for me to go back to that house today. I sometimes wonder if the people who live there have any idea of the massive foundations beneath them. Is a house like a car, where the owner's manual is passed on? When my father sold the house and moved to the city, for safety, did he leave behind the architect's drawings that I remember he traded for legal advice? I wonder what kind of fuel is fed to the Aga these days.

The cooker was part of the early morning ritual all right, but he didn't begin his dawn risings with it. It was bought and installed, like the Tea-Cal gesture, in recognition of this quirk in his nature. Sometimes he spent the early morning writing letters to his brothers and sisters in distant parts of Africa. Sometimes he went out and washed the car, surprising and perhaps troubling Wanjiko, the garden woman, whose daily chore it was. She would arrive, plump and shining with smiles, usually dragging one or two of her youngest illegitimate children by the hand, and she'd stop... amazed, annoyed perhaps, or even feeling criticized, at the sight of Bwana in the early morning light, naked except for gumboots and a towel wrapped around his waist, sloshing the shammy back and forth across the grey roof of the Humber Super Snipe. She'd stop, and her body would sag, as much as to say: "Auw...now what do *I* do? Raking. Always bloody leaves!" Then she'd burst into actual speech, picking up the conversation from yesterday or the day before. And he, like the headman of the village, chatting, dignified and without snobbery, to the village whore, would turn from the car, stand ungainly in the mud, the shammy dangling from his right hand, his left hand scratching at a nipple on his hairless chest, or at the side of his neck, and talk back. My bedroom window looked out on the scene, and one day I noticed him there chatting to Wanjiko, and later, when I finished my tea and was coming back from the kitchen with a second cup, I saw them still there chatting. It surprised me, considering the difficulties of communication between them. Struggling, both of them, with the pidgin Swahili which was no more her mother tongue than it was his, but the only language they had in common, they would manage conversations like this:

FATHER: Many, many birds come in the night past, huh?
WANJIKO: Birds?
FATHER: Yes, many birds.
WANJIKO: Birds of Europeans, *rrrr*, in the sky?
FATHER: Oh no, no! (waving elbows, shaking head) Birds...made
of...meat. *Cheep-cheep!*

WANJIKO: Ohh! You mean *birds!*
FATHER: Yes! Many come in the night past.
WANJIKO: Oh. Where they come?
FATHER: *There!* (pointing into gum trees above servants' quarters)
     In the trees! You no hear? Many, many! *Elfu mingi!* Thousands!
WANJIKO: Oh. Myself no hear.
FATHER: No?
WANJIKO: Oh. . .that month of yesterday?
FATHER: (waving arms wildly) No! No! No! This night past now!
WANJIKO: No hear them. *Hapana sikia.*
FATHER: Hapana sikia?
WANJIKO: *Hapana sikia.*
FATHER: Very strange.
WANJIKO: Yes, very strange!

All this while, Wanjiko's silent children, naked but for an undershirt, just as father is naked but for his big old car-washing towel and his gumboots, are staring at him, hands in their mouths and the fingers covered with drool, or unconsciously tugging at a foreskin. Their wide eyes make rings of startling white around the black pupils. They never seem to get used to the surprise of *mzungu*'s skin, especially like this, without clothes. That strange, unwholesome, sickly pink, their eyes seem to say, how can you bear to live with that?

Later, at breakfast, through his toast, my father mumbles, with a puzzled frown on his face, that Wanjiko must be drinking again: "You know she didn't even hear the starlings last night? A million of the buggers, kicking up that shindig right above her—I think they'd have to land in her hair for that woman to notice!"

Meanwhile, in the kitchen, Wanjiko is talking in through the window: "The old man's going crazy. Not enough sleep. He wakes up dreaming of birds, and goes out and washes his car in the middle of the night!"

It was that one day, seeing Wanjiko and my father chatting, and twenty minutes later still chatting, that I realized he wasn't so much washing the car as waiting for someone to arrive and talk to him of simple things. I saw that it wasn't just a habit or a quirk of his nature that made him get up in the morning when everyone was still asleep, and make tea, or write letters, or prune the coffee. Dawn was a special time for him. As though he sensed everything beginning to go wrong in the world, in history, in his life; but that for a few moments at dawn it was possible to enter another world and have the illusion of living there. As though, yes, the sun does rise very day like clockwork on us, and *one of these days, by God*, the morning is going to angle off on a different track, to a world where people talk openly to one another from the heart, and such intimacy is normal, not a gift; a world where people agree, instead of this constant wrangling; a world in which things are made properly, and they *work*.

In the family, it goes back at least to his mother, The Missus. When she stayed with us after my mother's death, and it was the first time I met her, she would come in to breakfast with her long white hair dangling loose around the faded lapels of her blue dressing gown (which she wouldn't give up for the new ones he bought her) and her reading glasses pushed up on her forehead.

"I'll give you some money for the stamps," she'd say, and hand my father twenty letters to mail.

"Good heavens, *no*, Missus!" He was always so proud of her for this. "I'll stamp and mail them, you've done your bit *writing* them. What time were you up?" Then he'd begin looking through the addresses to see if she'd made a mistake with a box number, or written Salisbury instead of Bulawayo.

"Oh...three."

He'd frown. He'd carp: "But, Missus, you were reading late last night. You can't burn it at both ends of the candle like that. You'll do yourself no good."

He himself was in no such danger. Except when I was a very small child and I remember once, waking scared in the middle of the night, and came in on him bent over his legal papers at the dining-room table, his old rectangular briefcase open on the chair beside him—except for that once, I can't remember a night when my father was home and not in bed by seven or eight o'clock. If you had to go in and tell him some important thing you'd suddenly remembered, you'd find him with a pillow clamped around his head, his elbow sticking up in the air, almost asleep, with the radio beside him quietly droning (*"Sheffield United, three; West Bromwich Albion, nil"*).

Sometimes, in the morning, he would bring me in a cup of tea. Whenever my brother was home too, from school or university, you could count on it. But especially in the bleak period after my mother's death and before he married again, after The Missus had been and gone, when all the servants, except the cook and Wanjiko, had been given a paid leave of several months, and father and I were alone in the house a lot, he would seek me out. He'd come to my bedroom at dawn with tea, levering down the handle with his elbow, a cup in each hand, watching not to spill, and beginning, "You see..." as though this were the second sentence, as though he'd stated his topic in the sentence before and was now starting to amplify it; or else we were in the middle of a conversation begun yesterday. "You see, I don't believe there's much point in going to The Coast in April, if the Long Rains are anything like last year. That's the trouble with this darn country, you never know if the rains are going to snooker you. You see, it goes in about a seven-year cycle...." Then he'd be taking the rain record book from under his arm and showing me last year and the year before: "See there, two-point-eight, and—put that other light on, boy, you'll strain your eyes." By the time he'd finished his tea, and yet another explanation of his theory of the rain cycle, or the morality cycle ("See, its *all* a pendulum"), or later, when I'd turned fourteen and begun to drive on the side roads, his key to safe driving ("Now Uncle Doc says: 'The road is mine till somebody else wants it,' but he belongs to a different generation, you see, with fewer cars. Today you have to make the assumption that *everybody else on the road is a bloody fool*, and *that's* how you drive. Otherwise, one second and pffft! Peanut butter! I see them come in again and again to the office, and it takes years to get the insurance settlements!"), or his lecture on how to save brake linings by gearing down for hills, and he'd set down his empty cup...at last, he'd feel content. He'd go off and read the rain gauge, or prune the coffee, or even drive in to the office early. And I'd go back to sleep.

It was as though the dawn that he got up for every day (counting on the one damn thing in the world that *did* work, the Aga)—as though the dawn provoked thoughts in him that he *must* share. And he did not know how. He struggled to speak...and it came out rainfall, brake linings, or a complete explanation of the workings of an electric bell....

All this happened thirty years ago and more. My father's been dead more than ten. My life is now on the other side of the world, in Canada. But here, I sit at the kitchen table. It's dawn. I write. And, as I write, memories come back to me that were lost: Wanjiko's bursting, innocent smile; the din of glossy starlings wheeling about the gum trees at dusk, and the sudden silence after they land; the weight of those big chromed covers on the Aga, and the blast of heat. And I'm thinking of a picture I took. God knows where all those old snapshots ended up, but I can see this one clearly. It's a picture of my father, taken from behind, in the early morning. He's leaning in to the engine of the Wolseley 14 parked under a mango tree, probably drying off the distributor cap. He's barefoot and naked, except that around his middle he wears the evidence of the only deliberate indiscretion of his life: his long, ragged, beloved car-washing towel, with the thick blue stripes down the centre, in which one can plainly read the words NYALI BEACH HOTEL—stolen, I think, because it was a place increasingly frequented by Americans and various other hoity-toity foreigners.

MARGARET ATWOOD

*Margaret Atwood is of course one of the country's most versatile and productive writers. She is a poet, novelist, and short-story writer; she has published an influential critical work (*Survival*) and an essential anthology (*The New Oxford Book of Canadian Verse in English*). In her many roles she has been a frequent contributor to* Anthology *— as a poet, short-story writer, and commentator on the literary scene.*

The three poems printed here are from Margaret Atwood's Journals of Susanna Moodie. *This long poem was broadcast on* Anthology *in 1969, in a reading by Mia Anderson. A recording of that reading is available from CBC Enterprises, and the poem was published in 1970 by Oxford University Press.*

✤

Further Arrivals

After we had cross the long illness
that was the ocean, we sailed up-river

On the first island
the immigrants threw off their clothes
and danced like sandflies

We left behind one by one
the cities rotting with cholera,
one by one our civilized
distinctions

and entered a large darkness.

It was our own
ignorance we entered.

I have not come out yet

My brain gropes nervous
tentacles in the night, sends out
fears hairy as bears,
demands lamps; or waiting

for my shadowy husband, hears
malice in the trees' whispers.

I need wolf's eyes to see
the truth.

I refuse to look in a mirror.

Whether the wilderness is
real or not
depends on who lives there.

Death of a Young Son by Drowning

He, who navigated with success
the dangerous river of his own birth
once more set forth

on a voyage of discovery
into the land I floated on
but could not touch to claim.

His feet slid on the bank,
the currents took him;
he swirled with ice and trees in the swollen water

and plunged into distant regions,
his head a bathysphere;
through his eyes' thin glass bubbles

he looked out, reckless adventurer
on a landscape stranger than Uranus
we have all been to and some remember.

There was an accident; the air locked,
he was hung in the river like a heart.
They retrieved the swamped body,

cairn of my plans and future charts,
with poles and hooks
from among the nudging logs.

It was spring, the sun kept shining, the new grass
lept to solidity;
my hands glistened with details.

After the long trip I was tired of waves.
My foot hit rock. The dreamed sails
collapsed, ragged.

> I planted him in this country
> like a flag.

The Immigrants

They are allowed to inherit
the sidewalks involved as palmlines, bricks
exhausted and soft, the deep

lawnsmells, orchards whorled
to the land's contours, the inflected weather

only to be told they are too poor
to keep it up, or someone
has noticed and wants to kill them; or the towns
pass laws which declare them obsolete.

I see them coming
up from the hold smelling of vomit,
infested, emaciated, their skins grey
with travel; as they step on shore

the old countries recede, become
perfect, thumbnail castles preserved
like gallstones in a glass bottle, the
towns dwindle upon the hillsides
in a light paperweight-clear.

They carry their carpetbags and trunks
with clothes, dishes, the family pictures;
they think they will make an order
like the old one, sow miniature orchards,
carve children and flocks out of wood

but always they are too poor, the sky
is flat, the green fruit shrivels
in the prairie sun, wood is for burning;
and if they go back, the towns

in time have crumbled, their tongues
stumble among awkward teeth, their ears
are filled with the sound of breaking glass.
I wish I could forget them
and so forget myself:

my mind is a wide pink map
across which move year after year
arrows and dotted lines, further and further,
people in railway cars

their heads stuck out of the windows
at stations, drinking milk or singing,
their features hidden with beards or shawls
day and night riding across an ocean of unknown
land to an unknown land.

MORLEY
CALLAGHAN

A TALK ON GABRIEL GARCÍA MÁRQUEZ

The novelist and short-story writer Morley Callaghan, who also has had a long and distinguished career as a broadcaster, contributed a monthly talk to Anthology *from the early 1970s until 1983. His subjects in these spoken essays were his fellow writers in Canada and abroad, the craft of writing itself, and anything else that attracted his wide-ranging interest. Many of Mr. Callaghan's short stories have also been heard on the program during its thirty-year history.*

Morley Callaghan's most recent novel is A Time for Judas *(Macmillan, 1983). A paperback edition of the book will be published in the fall of 1984 by Avon.*

❖

The discovery of a great writer has always filled me with wonder and curiosity. It is hard to do something so new with words and style that the book comes out all of a piece in its own sense of reality. Genius is there when the method, or the way the material is caught and looked at, seems to depend simply on the inner eye of the artist. This great writer, who was new to me, though known no doubt to thousands, is Gabriel García Márquez, the South American author of *One Hundred Years of Solitude*. The only other South American whose work is familiar to me is Jorge Luis Borges. Borges is celebrated internationally; laurel wreaths are placed on his brow wherever he goes. He is a great craftsman who translates beautifully; his style so finely honed that you must at least salute him as an artist when you finish one of his little stories. Yet for me Borges offers none of the fresh sense of wonder I get from Márquez. Borges is full of echoes from Europe, echoes from nineteenth-century European idealistic philosophy. From him I get no sense of discovery, only my recognition of his craving for perfection.

But this man Márquez, he bursts upon you with all the wild opulence of the jungle, the swamp, the crazy dreams of people, their piety, their brutality, their amazing courage, their betrayals and loyalties. The talent comes at you with the rush of a torrent, such a rush that a reader accustomed to English literature draws back at first, thinking, Oh, this is all too exotic, and then caught up he perceives that he is in the wild flow of limitless life. Mind you, dreams and fantasies and tall tales, miracles and nonsense, are a part of every man's life. We know this. And here it is. With his masterly style Márquez has achieved this extension of reality. He has done it in a way far beyond the scope of the naturalistic writer.

I'm not concerned with the factual story of *One Hundred Years of Solitude*. The outline gives none of the book's flavour. It is a story about the birth and death of a mythical South American town called Macondo. Where is it? Maybe in Ecuador. Maybe in any other country in Latin America. It is the story, too, of the rise and fall of the Buendía family. The founder of the town, old José Buendía, is succeeded by his son Colonel Buendía, who makes endless revolutions, is defeated again and again, keeps coming back, triumphs, sees the eternal failure of his revolution, becomes a national hero, then suffers in his awareness that revolutionary triumph is a kind of ghastly tragic joke. His town is rotting in the corruption all around him. But outlasting all the wild political events, all the lust and the follies of the town, all the births and deaths, the mad fantasies, the famines, the executions, is Úrsula, the mother. Úrsula, the mother. Úrsula, the wife of the town's founder. And what a great character she is. She is the eternal wife, the everlasting mother, with her own superstitious sense of earthly reality. The prosaic one, holding the family together with her own completely feminine wisdom. For me, in Úrsula's hundred years, she is almost crying out, "Before the town was, a woman was, before all the wild fantasies of men with their lust and crazy political brutalities, a woman was"; and when her men in their dreams are wildly on the side of death she is prudently trying to husband her own bit of soil. Her house, her family, her faith must survive, as she survives till the time comes when she is old and blind. Even then, while the life flickers on in her, she knows her house so well that her kinfolk are compelled to forget she is blind.

Úrsula the mother is among the great characters of fiction. I am emphasizing her as a character while really being interested now in the wonder of the Márquez method, because Úrsula's ancient, hard, unyielding female sense of reality seems to give a splendid balance of conviction to this factual style. Here then is what fascinated me. If you are going to do the chronicle of a mythical town covering a hundred years, how do you do a job that will convey all the superstitions, all the lying, all the lust, all the massacres in a straight, naturalistic style, or even in the poetic style of a Turgenev? The particular psyches of the characters would be separated, as people are separated. We would know when one character was dreaming, one telling the truth, another telling lies. When it was all put down this way we would be able to see that behind the putting down was the author's own critical sense of reality— something apart, making us aware of the difference between fact and fantasy.

But Márquez with a magnificent insight into the power of style, a power that can create its own transcendent reality, handled the problem with the quick sureness of genius. The story, then, is to be told in a straightforward lucid, natural style. Using this style, Márquez is as literal as Tolstoy. The journey, the march that results in the founding of the town, is done as directly, as factually, as Xenophon did it in the March of the Ten Thousand. The recording of events. Now here is the trick. What are the events in the life of a town, any town, any life? Simply the provable facts that might be noted by any rational bookkeeper? Ah, no.

Rather the events of this mythical town are the things that happened and the things the people imagined happened, and the things that became legend, and, as legend, later on became facts; and the lies too, related as facts so that they are believed later on and not to be questioned. These things, I say, are put down in a literal style, all as events given equal weight. Sometimes the telling is very terse. A wonder is related laconically. A girl is said to have vanished at her death, a direct ascension into the clouds, no doubt: this is told as casually as the naturalistic telling of how another girl sucked her thumb. And from this style so devoid of all psychological probing, of all the baggage of fidelity to the naturalist flow of thought, comes a startling real picture of the soul of a community, the swirl of life, a more complete life without and within the strange figures we call men and women. And with this style, treating all things great and small as fact, pure fact, everything is in motion, all is action.

A woman who had read this book said to me, "But surely it is all symbolic. Surely the old man's obsession with his life's work, the fine metalwork, the making of little fish out of gold, surely that stands for the church, doesn't it?" Fish: the church? "I don't know," I said. And another reader said to me, "When the old man grows old and senile, they put a rope around his neck and tie him to a tree in the sunlight, where he lives out his days. Surely that has some great symbolic meaning." Maybe. Again, I don't know. I look at these things as part of the whole, part of the fantastic town life, part of the imagination. I seek and recognize the fantastic unity of the book, an original work, a rare thing. Let the academics, if they will, take it to pieces, symbol by symbol, till the unity of the imagination is torn to shreds. I like to feel the unbroken impact of this great writer, keeping incredibly the child's sense of wonder, held only by the spell of his magic method.

HELEN WEINZWEIG

Helen Weinzweig was born in Poland and came to Toronto at the age of nine. She is married to the composer John Weinzweig. She began publishing fiction in her middle age, her first novel, Passing Ceremony, *in 1973 and a second novel,* Basic Black With Pearls, *in 1980. Her short stories have appeared in* Saturday Night, *the* Canadian Forum, Toronto Life, *and other magazines. "Causation" was commissioned by the CBC for broadcast in a series of new stories on* Anthology *and published in* Small Wonders *(CBC Enterprises, 1982).*

✿

Causation

The woman hesitated at first to let him in. "Piano tuner," Gyorgi Szigeti said, then waited, leaning against the door frame. He waited for her to decide whether he was a musician and therefore eligible to come in the front door, or whether he was a tradesman to be directed to the rear entrance. What she could not have known was that Gyorgi had no intention of using the servants' entrance. He stood before her, proud in his black bowler hat, his long white silk scarf knotted loosely and flowing down over his shiny black leather jacket. "Piano tuner," he repeated to the woman, who had not moved. She was transfixed. "Oh my God," she said, "not you, not you!" He did not question her words: by habit he took no notice of the eccentricities of the rich. Slowly, slowly, she widened the doorway.

No one ever had to show him where the piano was. He found it the way a dog searches out a bone. Traversing miles, it seemed, of Oriental carpets to reach the ebony grand piano at the other end of a vast room, he experienced a numbness, a detachment, as if asleep and dreaming: he had a sense of having once before covered the distance. And the short, sturdy woman in a flowered housecoat (he had noticed) who was following him—he knew her, too. But then, he knew a lot of women, some also short and sturdy, and maybe that's all it was: so many women.

"It's my own piano," she was saying. Her heavy hand clumped across the keys. "This B keeps getting out of tune," striking the note five times to let him hear how bad it was.

Gyorgi Szigeti almost fell to his knees. He was in the presence of a Bechstein grand piano.

She was still talking. "Everything you see in here, all the furniture in the house, was chosen by my ex-husband. He lets me keep my piano only because he is a music lover."

Gyorgi removed his black leather jacket, draping it on the back of a gilded chair with curved legs. The bowler hat and silk scarf he arranged carefully on the seat. He ran his fingers over the piano keys. The sound was as brilliant as he remembered a Bechstein to be; the bass was resonant and the top notes vibrant. This was unexpected: in these wealthy homes the pianos were regarded as furniture and tuned only when an anticipated house guest was some sort of performer.

"I'm a singer. A concert artist. An opera star," she announced. "That is, I used to be an opera star."

While Gyorgi worked, she sat on the piano bench, which he had moved aside. She hummed each note in unison with his repeated plunking as he tightened strings. She had perfect pitch. It spurred him on, this breathless attention of hers; then the two of them listening, listening together, both now intent on the climactic moments when he brought each white whole note and each black half note to perfection. He felt like the Creator of All Sound. When he tightened a string, he had a way of tightening his mouth, twisting the left corner upward into his cheek, which resulted in a threatening grimace. Once the ideal sound was achieved, his mouth loosened.

She rose to leave. "Would you like some coffee?"

Gyorgi looks around, then re-enters the room in his mind, retraces his steps in imagination; but this time, instead of seeing her figure stride out the doorway, as it is doing at this very moment, he sees her laid out in a satin-lined coffin, in the same flowered housecoat; and instead of her sluttish make-up, the face in death is delicately tinted as if in the blush of youth. The mortician's skill has fixed the happiness he, Gyorgi, gave her. After the funeral he stays on in the old house, sleeping in one of the spare rooms, surprised at his delicacy, even in fantasy, in not using the bedroom where he had made her ecstatic. The letter from the lawyers comes, addressed to Gyorgi Szigeti, to this house. She has left him everything. Every-thing, including the beloved Bechstein, is his. Just in time, before her return interrupts his fateful vision, he recalls with a sudden clarity the source of his images: an account in this morning's newspaper: rich elderly widow...a young man of thirty-three... they married...she died...left him everything she owned...great wealth...her daughters suing...old mother was crazy..."*They're* crazy," the new heir had protested to the judge, "she was more fascinating, more of a woman, than those two dried-up broads will ever be if they live to be a hundred."

Over coffee, perhaps because he had already lived out the scene in his mind, Gyorgi leaned forward and said in a voice deep with sincerity:

"You are still a beautiful woman. You have so much to give..."

She eyed him silently. She was about fifty-five, but in her clear, light eyes, raised to meet his directly, age had been postponed. It was a matter of pride with him that in his persuasions Gyorgi rarely lied. In every woman he found qualities he could honestly admire. He went on, emboldened:

"Your eyes—they are the eyes of a girl."

She denied nothing: that was all that mattered.

"These Bechsteins," he ventured, "do not take kindly to the extreme cold and intense heat of our climate. The wood...changes of temperature..." He brought out a small notebook from his back pocket. He could come back next week. To see if the tuning held.

Uppermost in her mind is the fact that his wide, curved mouth is at odds with his small, deep-set, dark eyes, suggesting to her an easygoing cruelty.

At his ring the following week she flung open the door. Her face was heavier than before with rouge and lipstick, her brows blacker, her lids greener. Gyorgi believed that if he ate enough of the stuff women put on their faces he would get cancer. In such cases he would put his lips to the bare hollows of her throat.

Today she ignored his pretence of tuning the perfectly tuned instrument. She didn't listen; she chattered.

"Once I was Violetta with the San Francisco Opera Company. Oswald, my former husband, loved *Traviata*. He loved me. He offered me the world if I would give up the stage and sing for him alone: wealth, babies, a fire in the hearth on Sunday nights. Oh, he knows his operas...I worked hard, practised every day. In the evening, with the two babies asleep in the nursery, I sang for him. I dressed for the part. The costumes accumulated: Cio-Cio San, Carmen, Tosca, Mignon.

"The idyll lasted almost five years. One morning I awoke to find him standing at the foot of the bed. The room was still dark so that I could not quite see his face, just the outline of his figure, fully dressed. He had been waiting, I sensed, for me to awaken. I sat up and then he spoke, slowly and distinctly:

" 'You are not the great artist I thought you were. You cannot place your voice, and when it comes out from behind your big nose, the glorious music falls to the floor like a bag of cement. You are ridiculous in the clothes of the great heroines: you have the passion of a disposable lighter. You have deceived me.' With that he left and never returned."

"Did he leave you for another woman?" Gyorgi asked, for that is what he knew of the way of the world.

"No, no, he wouldn't do that. He is a very respectable man."

"Did he marry again?"

"Ha! The only woman he'd consider would have to be a virgin who chose marriage to Oswald instead of entering a nunnery." She gave him a sly smile. "You know what? I think Oswald was jealous of my music. When I played the role of Mimi or Aïda or Desdemona, I became the woman I was portraying. I didn't mean to, but I escaped him each time—*that's* what he couldn't stand."

Gyorgi tilted his head in a pretence of interest. He had no idea what she was talking about, but he realized that she was determined to reveal herself to him. It was as if women had to expose themselves—their defeats, their triumphs, their hopes and beliefs—before they undressed. In his opinion, a nude man in a raincoat was more honest. Gyorgi listened to women for their "tone" quality, the same way he listened when he was tuning a piano. He noticed that her forehead glistened with perspiration.

"I can't pay you today," she said. "Oswald has gone to India to see his guru. Left me without a cent. Again."

"It's all right," he said gently, "you can pay me any time."

Even after she had paid him, Gyorgi took to dropping in, making his visits sporadic, so that they would seem compulsive, as if he couldn't resist seeing her. She was always unprepared, and would run to comb her hair and put on fresh lipstick. One he stopped her, saying he liked her the way she was. Above all, he would want her to be perfectly natural with him. She was so moved by these sentiments, she wanted to do something for him in return.

"Would you like to hear Cio-Cio San's farewell aria? No? I see. But you obviously know everything about pianos."

"I was an apprentice for five years in the Bechstein factory in Berlin."

"What else can you do?"

"I can build a bomb shelter."

"Good. Then you can take care of this house. What do you say—live here and look after things. Oh, you will go out to your work as you always have, but instead of a small room in a smelly boarding-house—ah, I thought so!—you can stay here. Pick any of the five spare rooms. What do you say?"

Gyorgi couldn't speak. He put his hands on his lap lest she see how they shook. A mansion, a Bechstein—all within the space of a few weeks. He hung his head and assumed the obsequious manner of his youth.

Then he went through the house, taking the stairs two at a time. The rooms were full of the kind of masterpieces he had seen only behind thick silken cords in museums. Everything was old and massive or old and fragile; everything was forceful with value. She ran after him, unable to keep up, observing that he moved with an animal grace, as if he had lived all his life out of doors.

"I can't understand why a man would want to leave you. It's a wonderful house," he said.

"Oswald doesn't care about material things—furniture, cars, clothes—he has no interest in them. He wants to touch the infinite, discover the ineffable; he is on a journey of the spirit, he is concerned only with his immortal soul."

"So?" said Gyorgi. "So?" he repeated. "He has never had to work hard in order to eat."

"You must know that I still love him."

Suddenly she was crying, crying for no reason that he could see.

He waved an arm into the air, around and around. "You have everything; you have it all!"

"Nothing! Nothing, I tell you. There is only the music, notes on a page, enduring, eternal, nothing else exists." Then, in after-thought, her voice distant, she added, "You are the exception."

He chose the sixth bedroom. Hers. Awaiting her in the wide bed, he called out, "And wash that damned crap off your face."

When she came back into the room, she grasped the post at the foot of the huge bed, weaving slightly as if drunk, and intoned:

"I adore you, you are low-born, you have no character, you are inevitable. Ours will be an affair of terrible limits. Your insults are without principle. Whatever grief you will cause will come natu-rally and I shall recover as one does after slipping on ice. Most

97

important, though, Oswald will no longer be able to draw blood with his blunt knives. I shall continue to go to him every week for money. But it will be for you. That will make it easy. No. More than that. I shall *enjoy* the humiliation. I will answer his interrogation: 'Why is the butcher's bill so high?' 'Because I have a tall, strong man to feed,' I will sit in the leather chair in his office while he counts out the ten-dollar bills, slowly, sliding them halfway across the desk. I will lean forward and scoop them up and thank him. Oswald will unbutton his vest and look across at me like a judge with a three-time loser and condemn me, as he always does, with good advice. But I won't care. He has lost his power: tonight I hand it over to you."

During the prolonged love-making that follows, she opens her eyes a few times. Once she sees his mouth tighten and a corner go up into his cheek into an ugly grimace.

Gyorgi moved in. It was then that he was faced with what he had missed that first time because his head had been bursting with the delirium of his good fortune. There was everywhere a fury of disorder, as if a bomb had gone off in each room separately. The halls had boxes and overshoes strewn about. There was dirt on every surface; old dust that had hardened; mouse droppings in the kitchen and cockroaches in the sinks. She shrugged off his dismay. "Oswald won't pay for a cleaning woman."

Gyorgi loved control and completeness. He set about to restore order, spending every weekend sweeping, scrubbing, repairing, room by room, starting with the bedroom. The kitchen alone took a month. The cellar, he figured, could occupy him as long as she lived.

There was no design to her life. Asleep when he left, off in a world of song when he got home; she could not remember what, if anything, she had accomplished, nor what had transpired during the day. "Some phone calls. Nothing much. How was *your* day?" And showered him with kisses. One of the phone calls, he surmised, was for the frozen chicken pie and canned pea soup that he was eating for dinner. And he, who required a daily pattern to blanket his years, felt a chill of apprehension.

"Now, my handsome Magyar," she crooned, "I'll sing for you and you alone. I learned some Hungarian folk songs set by Kodály."

"I told you a dozen times, I hate Hungarian anything. Maybe there's a soccer game on TV."

"Don't you ever tire of watching grown men kick a ball?"

"You have the memory of an imbecile: I told you: I was a professional soccer player. I toured Germany."

Each day Gyorgi went out on his calls. He had given up his black leather jacket and now wore a navy blue blazer with a crest embroidered in red and white on the upper left pocket. He refused to part with his bowler hat and long white scarf. He no longer said, "Piano tuner" at the front door. Instead, he presented, wordlessly, his business card with his name and elegant new address and *Pianos Tuned to Perfection* embossed in shiny black script. As the days got shorter, he came home earlier and earlier. Some cold days he did not go out at all. He would float about the house, content to hammer, force windows open, stop taps from dripping. She would follow him around like the small daughter he once had. While he worked, she would sit on the floor, always in the flowered housecoat, telling him stories about people she knew.

"You're making it up," he sometimes accused her. "No, no," she protested, "that's what he really did." Or, "She was desperate. A woman in that state will say anything." His disbelief at times bordered on wonder: did people of wealth and substance really carry on crazy like that? Keeping his eyes on his work, never turning his head, pretending a lofty indifference, he would probe with ruttish questions: what had taken place with her and Oswald in bed; what had she done with other men; how many lovers; in what combinations. And she, without a second thought, would lay open intimacies as one spreads open an umbrella in the rain. And always she hugged her knees and chortled deep in her throat, "But you, my darling, are the best, you are the champ." On those days a camaraderie was struck between them and he felt himself to be her equal in the sense that she was no better than he. More than that: he felt himself elevated, and ceased to regret, once and for all, that he was so unschooled that she had to read to him the instructions on a can of varnish.

Every night he made love to her. He treated the whole business as his part of the bargain. In bed his movements were as easy and graceful as when he painted a wall or repaired a broken drainpipe. He was precise; he was unhurried. Afterwards, Gyorgi would turn over as if fatigued, although his exultation was boundless. He did this rather than listen to her. "You talk too much," he would say, "people screw up by talking too much."

Once she frightened him in the middle of the night by shaking him awake. The bedside lamp was on. She was sitting bolt upright.

"Quickly," she said in an urgent voice, "don't think, tell me, quickly, what is life?"

"Life," he said obediently, "is. Life is. That's all. You're either alive or dead."

"Wrong!" she said sharply. "Life is an imposition. Oswald refuses to admit it. He wants life to be raw, with the bones showing. Today he presented me with a new account book, with more spaces for more entries. He threatened me again: unless I am more exact about the money I spend, he will cut off my alimony. He *imposes* himself on my life."

Gyorgi condescended. "What are you complaining about? A short ride in the Mercedes and you're living fat for another week. Perfect octaves don't buy houses like this."

"You comprehend nothing." She turned from him. "You know nothing of the malice that masquerades as virtue. You are young: you still make plans."

He stared at the long, heavy drapes.

"After the war we were thrown out of Hungary and shipped in boxcars to Germany. We lived behind barbed wire, then in barracks, then in a shack somewhere outside Frankfurt. All night long we heard the screams of the tortured. My brothers and sisters and I jumped out of bed when we heard the cries. We took turns standing on a chair at the small, high window. We could see nothing. Our parents never woke up."

She studied him: there was no humility in him. She laid her head on his chest and a hand on his shoulder. Gyorgi yawned and lay back with his hands under his head.

"Fate," she whispered, "weaves its mysteries in the dark; that is why we do not know our destiny in the light of day."

"That's true," he agreed, understanding nothing. He had no sense of the abstract, but he recognized, if not destiny, certainly an opportunity. "You have a beautiful house. I'm surprised you never married again."

"Oswald wouldn't like it. Besides, if I married I wouldn't have this beautiful house."

Gyorgi, startled, heard only the first part: "Oswald wouldn't like it." What did Oswald have to do with her desire to marry again? His own life had been a series of divorcements so immutable that he never again saw his parents, his brothers and sisters, two wives, countless lovers, as well as a number of unreasonable employers. If his decision to part, made simply and honestly, was challenged, he used his soccer-field fists, elbows, knees, or boots to make his meaning clear.

"We are lovers now," he pursued, "let us be as if married. I will care for you as my father did for my mother; you will care for me as my mother did my father."

"But you are already here, in my house, in my bed. . ."

Lack of sleep made Gyorgi irritable. She was missing the point.

"From now on," he rasped, "you will do a woman's work."

"Oh, oh," she moaned, "more impositions. . ."

"We must speak of necessities," he went on inexorably. "Food is a necessity. Respect is a necessity. It is necessary to respect the place you eat and sleep in. The way you live now, you turn roses into shit. Starting tomorrow, you will keep the house clean, wash the clothes, cook the meals. I will take out the garbage, attend the mousetraps, spray the roach powder."

"My music. . ."

"*Deine Stimme is zum Kotzen*," he said as day dawned, "you have the voice of a crow."

"Yes, yes," she said, falling in with his thought, "I will buy a loom and learn to weave."

"Don't be stupid. You're too clumsy."

She flung her faith into the new day. Laughing now and clapping her hands she exclaimed:

"You noticed! Oh, how I do love you!"

She no longer rouges her lips and cheeks nor colours her eyelids. Gyorgi has convinced her of his preference for an unadorned face. This he has done by holding her head down in the bathroom sink filled with water. Her giggles spluttered, she choked, she lost consciousness. She has learned that he means what he says. She thinks he has helped her begin a new life. She telephones everyone she knows to tell them that she gets up in the morning and that she bakes bread.

Just before Christmas there was a party. Gyorgi was surprised, considering her indolence, that she had so many friends. Well, maybe he could understand: she was guileless; she harboured no ill will. He was sent to the convenience store on Summerhill Avenue for peanuts and chips and mixes. "Not to worry," she assured him, "everyone brings a bottle. All we need are enough clean glasses." He went back and bought five dozen plastic glasses.

Gyorgi dressed for the evening. He wore a white shirt and a

patterned silk tie and real gold cuff links—gifts of grateful women. He looked distinguished, almost, in a suit. The synthetic brown cloth hung on his frame like an admiral's uniform. She introduced him: "Isn't he gorgeous!" He walked behind her and watched gravely while she went about kissing men and "adoring" them. In his turn he was careful not to flirt with women. He could take no chances: women mistook his compliments for confessions.

He assumed the dignity of the foreman he remembered in the Bechstein factory, hands behind his back, observing everyone, recording, alert to what might be expected of him. He mixed drinks, removed coats, and carried them upstairs; clipped pairs of galoshes and boots together with clothespins. After a while he realized that the guests made no distinction between him and themselves. An envoy from India invited him to a cricket match in Edwards Gardens next summer; Gyorgi invited him in return to a soccer match next summer, also in Edwards Gardens. A pretty psychiatrist wept on his breast in revealing an unhappy marriage; he told her of his own two divorces. A stockbroker took him aside, confided that metals were going to be big, and gave him a business card. Gyorgi went upstairs and got his business card, which he gave to the stockbroker. Gyorgi was overcome by a sophistication he had never known before. In his new expansiveness he slid into discussions.

"Hitler never wanted war," he said with the authority of one who also has an inside track to matters of importance. "He waited outside Poland for word from Chamberlain, who double-crossed him and declared war on Germany. The Allies have falsified history. Hitler could have invaded Britain but ordered the generals to hold off, always hoping for peace. The Holocaust was a lie, spread by Jewish international bankers."

She, meanwhile, had been circling. In the silence that followed his revelations she linked her arm through his and pulled him away just when he was about to heap fact upon startling fact. Tomorrow (he intends) he will tell her: "It is not respectful for a woman to interrupt a man when he is speaking. You must never do that again."

Instead, it was she who faced him when everyone had gone. She was calm; there was a hardness about her as she stood looking up at him without a flicker or a twinge: "You must never, never again reveal your fascism. I will not permit racist talk in my house."

When the spring sun began to stream through the shiny windows and the lawn gave off a yielding odour, Gyorgi, too, softened. He permitted her to sing for him in the evening, to wear costumes and a little make-up. She accompanied herself at the Bechstein, the rings on both hands flashing under the crystal lights. He listened to her stories of the operas, stories of terror and love and irony and death. He listened and planned. There would be the garden to attend to, storms to be taken down, screens to be installed, dining-room chairs to be repaired. Days of work; music and parties; nights of love. The picture of an old woman dying and leaving him her big house faded, then disappeared altogether.

This night she was dressed as Mimi, looking quite appealing, he thought, in a pink bonnet tied with satin ribbons under her chin. She looked girlish and demure. He even recognized the song in which Mimi asks for a muff to warm her poor, cold hands. Suddenly she broke off, rose abruptly from the piano, turned off the lights, lit a candle, and waving it high overhead, announced:

"I want to die slowly like Mimi." She placed the candle on the table at the side of his chair and sank at his feet. "Do you still want to marry me?"

"Marry me...?" Gyorgi repeated, and his voice broke. He saw himself answering the ring at the front door, raising his eyebrows, and, if necessary, directing the caller to the servants' entrance. Forgiveness flowed over him. In his mind he sent money to his mother and father to come for a visit to see what he had made of himself. Then would come his brothers and sisters, each in turn. He drew her up on his lap. He removed Mimi's bonnet and stroked her head.

She, dreaming: "I feel like Gretel," cradling into him, "we will be like Hansel and Gretel, alone in the forest. We will learn to live in innocence, like peasants, gathering nuts and berries, protected from evil by our happiness."

"You people," he said, shaking his head, "I love the way you people want to play poor, with your budgets and your diets, with your gurus and your torn jeans." Suddenly he became angry. "It is all one big lie: you people couldn't survive a day's hunger."

"I'm not pretending. When I marry, Oswald cuts off my alimony. This is his house, lock, stock, and four-poster. We will not be allowed to stay here." Her teeth were clamped together. "Oswald would never let us live in his house."

Gyorgi felt evicted, dislodged from a place in his head. Somehow he did not find it odd that he should be striking out at her. But she was off his lap and out of range with a swiftness that surprised him: she must have expected something like this.

"You tricked me!" he shouted. "The work...the hours...I

cleaned up your bloody mess. . .it was to have been for me, for me, damn you. . .all this time I was busting my ass for him. . .for *his* house. . ."

In his fury he lunged at her. She ran from him and he after her with his fists extended. His anger also brought confusion: images of her friends, lawyers and judges and others in high places before whom he was powerless: he could smell the acid of a jail cell. He heard a crash. He stopped in his tracks as if shot and he heard her laugh. She was standing with her back to the Bechstein, her rump on the keys, her arms flung out and back in a posture of protection. He was astounded that she knew so little about him after all these days and nights that she could think him capable of harming a Bechstein. He banged his knuckles against each other and did not touch her. He opened his fingers and let his arms hang.

"What will become of you?" she taunted. "You have been spoiled, spoiled by mahogany and fine linen and oil paintings on the walls. You are unfit now for rented rooms and tired waitresses and the hopes of check-out girls."

So. They had come to the end of the game. It made him sad: he had liked her: he could have been satisfied. Then, doglike, shaking the discovery off himself, he withdrew, walking backwards. Gyorgi kept going, backwards, stepping over the thick carpets for the last time.

Where she is standing, in her shabby Mimi gown, arms still extended against her beloved piano, dry-eyed, ears strained towards the sounds of Gyorgi's departure, she knows already she will soon sit across the desk from fair, florid Oswald. She hears already his instructions: no calls. Hears Oswald's voice without a rise in it saying: "What happened this time? Hmm. You got off easy. Give me the account." She knows, too, that Oswald will lace his pale fingers across his chest and quote for the hundredth time: " 'Even among galley slaves there were ten percent volunteers.' For God's sake, when will you stop inviting your own destruction." She sees already her hungry hand as it moves across the desk. She will take the money to keep her safe for yet another little while.

JOAN FINNIGAN

"May Day Rounds: Renfrew County" was broadcast on Anthology *in November, 1968. It is one of the many poems and stories that Joan Finnigan has written about Ontario communities: most often about the Ottawa Valley but also about Kingston, Kitchener, and Northern Ontario. Her devoted work in local history has been preserved in such books as* "I Come from the Valley" *and* Kingston: Celebrate This City. *She wrote a prize-winning screenplay for the National Film Board movie* The Best Damn Fiddler from Calabogie to Kaladar. *"May Day Rounds: Renfrew County" has been published in a collection of Joan Finnigan's poetry,* Living Together *(Fiddlehead Poetry Books, 1976).*

❖

May Day Rounds: Renfrew County

Sorrow of the last snows is still in the crevasses
of the hills humus-scented and in the damp darkling
              tangles
of the hepatica-woods bird-forbidden but the day
is the may-apple sun come at last to the reeling earth
swell of heat at the centre of sleeping beetles and being
something musical has a message of green mystic seismograph
there are black ducks sitting on the carillon waters
country gardens have been spaded and hoed seeds carouse
spacelings of impatience the girl on the porch has let down
              her hair
newly-washed in the same-day sun of the galloping prince
Purblind pioneer Lake Doré is not golden but blue
the maiden-naked blue of lakes before the leaves blow up
against the lonely beehive of the sky The Clarke Farm
is a Century Farm with a sign swinging at its gate
saying someone has climbed this homing-hill hunter

for a hundred years, his quiet beasts sharing
this stubborn vigil   beyond the lake-gate, the lane
labours straight up into the sky past newly-cut timbers
rocks   sheep-runs   mad-eyed sheep   stony suggestions
of fields to a hidden log-house on the high hill-crown
someone with a claw-hold on this side of the hill
is slipping on ice and mud   panting you come to a farm-yard
steaming piles of manure cursed and forgotten.

broken fences   light spaces of missing boards and beams
doors slapping loose against the barn-sides   many bronchial
                                                        man-days
someone is down on his knees and listening to the count
The stoop on the log-house is brown with sweet rain-rot
like the boards around an old pump   and the woman is afraid
she comes out of the daylight darkness of the little old house
like a ewe reflecting house-fire in her eyes   retreat
messages shouted back into the house   welfare is like sex
without love   it may be withdrawn at any time without reason
or notice   and then she moves to greet us wiping her hands
on her faded apron   she is very afraid that we have come
to take something away   to make less in this single room
of cracked and worn linoleum and things without places
peeling unpainted   broken unmended   torn irreparable
work beyond woman's hands   and a nest of three hot irons
on the wood-stove for the week's wash   a man named Job
coughs behind the curtain and moves his feet restlessly in bed
the woman stands skitterish in the middle of the kitchen
Jordan's voice reaches out to help—"How's your husband, Mrs.
                                                        Clarke?"
"Oh, no better, I'm afraid. He's keepin' no better at all, at all"—
(Christ the Martyr, here is thy servant of the hot-stove
hands wring over this wretched fortune and hearken an old pain
going back into the childhood nails of our hands and our feet)
"The children are all at school?" "Oh, yes, indeed, indeed—"
"And how are they doing?" "None too badly, none too badly—"
she switches the frying pans of green bacon on the stove

the woman has only two biting teeth and an ironing-board back
age beyond all chronological reckoning including
this day's addition of fear   but something opens her pores
and flashes an earlier self now—it is when she finds

that we have not come to take anything away   "Oh, yes
the Clarkes have been here a hundred years," she says
"that's my husband's family, three generations. Did you see
the Century Sign on the gate? The lawyer told us
one-hundred-and-twenty years" SHE HAS A MOMENT OF
                                                                    PRIDE

"I hear you grow apples here the size of pumpkins?"
she has ANOTHER moment standing by her cook-stove
with a battered array of potato pots scoured and at-the-ready
"yes, yes, the Spy apples like it here on the side
of the hill beside Lake Doré and our maple syrup was good
this year, too—let me give you some" (she wants to reward us
for calling on her and not taking anything away)
we demur   she insists   and brings out a twelve-ounce
                                                          whiskey bottle
full of the sweet spirits of the tall svelte vats
warm days and cold nights make love and sap comes trickling
                                                                    down
we move towards her garden now   shelved along the small
                                                          panes—
a hundred-and-twenty-years of moonlight and sunlight
falling on the floor and the faces of babies school-boys
brides mothers dancers cursers lovers wailers givers weepers
takers singers workers coffin-bearers buyers sellers
here this sainted shrine of scarlet geraniums and sweet pink clover
shoddies the room and lights up her eyes   reaches out
and illuminates the manure piles   defies this stony heritage
the man coughs behind the curtain   he has nothing to say
all his prayers have gone unanswered   the three irons nest
hot on the cook-stove   the eldest son aged twenty-one
is trapped here on this invisible farm   he is the sacrifice
on the mountain   alone in the barn he lets the cattle
have it with a pitch-fork

Mrs. Plath is brown as a rose-pip berry and merry
to greet you all her eighty-three years on the bush farm
and this morning down scrubbing her kitchen floor
out on the Green Lake Road she has not had a visitor
for three months and she flutters around the room
like a bird from wall to wall and perch to perch
until finally she settles in the rocking-chair and fastens
her eyes upon us as though we were feed   right off, she gives us

her theory of bald-headedness amongst modern men
"they wash too often now and dry it out and then it falls"
(and is this innocence some primitive pre-conscious intuition
of impotence? on May Day at eighty-three does desire rise
and swell in loneliness and turn a woman to scrubbing her floors
too often   the ritual cleanings and tidying of frustrations?)
she has been asked to get out an old ball-gown and dance
her hill-billy hey-day for Centennial Celebration at

Killaloe Station

her two-winged house is too big for two and when she goes
echoing into another room somewhere to get some

undecipherable papers

from the Department for us to decipher I whisper to Jordan
"But she can't be eighty-three! she moves like a woman of forty!"
"ERIC NEEDS HER"   Eric is her fifty-year-old unmarried son
the blind man who works this farm   when he ploughs she

walks

lilies of the fields in front of him with a white sheet
tied over her head   he can see the outline   together they

make

a straight furrow   an Easter of slow exultation struggle
She has other children in Toronto and Kitchener
and in Osceola where there are no Indians left. People come
from far and near in harvest-time to gather the cherries
and apples from this farm   the stream runs clear
by the cattle at the gate   not a chip in the yard
eyes of mother   hands of son   blended into unbelievable one
the lettuce is already in   Mrs. Plath won't bother us
with figuring out the letter from the Department
it's true that Neighbour Nelligan got an increase
but letters are such bothers and it never seems to end
send one to the Department and you get one right back again
and it seems you're never finished with writing and replying
do they never want to be done with mailing and stamping in

Ottawa?

maybe she WILL dig up an old Victorian dress and dance
a discovery dance for Centennial Celebration at Killaloe Station—
Eric is back working in the bush today—can't sit around, you

know—

too bad you missed him   (who is it today back there in the bush

walks in front of Eric the Blind with a white sheet tied over her
head
to give him light for the clearing and brushing?)

At this log-house, the log-house of the last days of the Timms
eight children raised and seven flown out of a four-room nest
at this house now knitted closely needing in their old age
the Timms' Javex bottles jiggle and bounce on the trees
along their lane   they have been made into bird-feeding
stations
two rare white-throated sparrows feed regally wind-swung
when we knock the peep-hole on the door is opened
and eyes appear—"Joe sent us   three bottles of Ballantyne's"
and this the way the Timms have saved heat here
for forty years and raised and set in flight seven children
out of this nest of four rooms   two up and two down
she opens the door quickly and welcomes us in
short woman grown square   special boot for her club foot
many hairs both black and white blossomed on her chin
eyes sharp as a hungry sparrow's   scurry and crumb the table
apologize the logs haven't had their spring white-wash
bid us sit and sit nervously with us crossing your arms
over your chest as older women do in the presence of those
whose brassieres perform expensively illusion by elastic

"And where's Mr. Timm today?"   "Oh, he's working again—"
such a smile of slow pride   such a warm stealing man-loving
slowly-unwinding smile of man-loving pride of the man
gentle as strength gone to work again   sixty-seven
July 1   job found   "he felt better and the man at the mill
said he'd take him on until the hot weather comes—
they have a new law now you know   the saw has to be fitted
with a whatchamacallit?—"   "A guard?"   "Yes, yes, a guard
and he won't fall into it again"   she laughs because he
is out working again on the saw and he is safe by the saw
"Are you getting your payments?"   "Well, not this month
you see—he's back working—so the payments stopped and we got
a letter—I can't make it out—here I'll get it for you—perhaps
you can tell me what these people are trying to say—
"Yes, well, now—Mrs. Timm—this just means the Department
has stopped payment until Mr. Timm's employer lets them know

what he is making on his job per month   then they will
                                                                    supplement
that according to your annual needs here   light heat food rent"
"But Willie's afraid of working too much and too long
and the payments will be cut off altogether then
and he's not well enough—he might go down again at his age—
he wants to work—you know that well enough—but the time
                                                                    might come—

and he can't figure out what's best—but he'd like to not pay
too much for wanting to work—and we don't know—we aren't
                                                                    edjicated people—"

"Well, Mrs. Timm—it is really very simple—very simple
                                                                    indeed—
the minute Mr. Timm stops work you notify the authorities
at the Welfare Department in Toronto because this is provincial
and not municipal and they, after proper investigations
begin procedures to set about re-organization of payments
and under the new legislation no matter what Mr. Timm makes
your income will be supplemented up to a required minumum
                                                                    level
for all your needs   but that will only be for a few months now
for you and Mr. Timm I see by the records here in my file
are almost ready for Old Age Pensions and so you would notify
the Welfare Department officials in Toronto that you are applying
for Old Age Pensions from the Pension Fund in Ottawa and then
the Welfare Department in Toronto will make adjustments on the
                                                                    payments
in accordance with the pension money you receive—and of
                                                                    course, Mrs. Timm—
you know that under the New Act as the wife of a recipient
of an Old Age Pension you are eligible for an allowance now
yourself—and so you must apply separately for that"

                                        Mrs. Timm proffers the back
of an envelope   "Would you write that down for me please
I don't quite understand   we aren't edjicated people
and I'd be hard put to tell THAT to Willie when he comes in—"
"WRITE IT DOWN!   No—Mrs. Timm—let me try to
                                                                    explain it again—
you take the letter you got today and you burn it in the fire

but only after you have copied out the address of Mr. Peter Piper
who so kindly sent it to you from Toronto re File No. 601286
and you write for the Saw-Mill Accounts to the Department
of Labour because your husband is working part-time at
                                                    Balaclava
and when you get the forms you ignore the questions
and send one copy to the third bird-feeding station
from the end of the lane and one copy to your husband's employer
who will sign it and send it on to the CBC c/o Wojeck
and you say 'we aren't getting our cheque' and they say
'we regret to inform you that Re your letter of April Fool's Day'
and you say that you understand the differences between
                                                    provincial
and municipal welfare—one comes out of the Park Plaza in
                                                    Toronto
and one is a relief line-up in 1929 and then you beg to inform
the Department of Deep Schemes and Confusions that the case
will have to be re-considered or re-opened in the light of
your forthcoming birthdays and that according to the New Social
Assistance Act, Section XLV, part 209B, sub-section 3006
you are searching the deed of your house for proof of birth
and in due course will be done out of   or done in entirely
and fitting game for the lawyers who will have to be called in
to unravel the tax situation since pensioners are,
according to the original code of Canada, taxable."

"Would you write that down, please?—No, well then
well maybe you could explain all that to my son, Bethel
he is terribly clever   the high-school principal at Cobden
and you pass that way going home so if you'd just go in
and explain I'd be so grateful   let me put
the kettle on for you   would you like the stove lit
I let it go out because I was so hot doing the washing"
the seven birds flown from the nest are on the wall
grandchildren smiling cheap photography in North Bay
Sunday dressed and stiffened in Kamloops, B.C.
Bethel the last of the birds, living at home, has begun
to cover the logs   put in walls   Mrs. Timm runs her hand
over the plaster   finished in part   painted pale green
you suddenly know a log-cabin woman's longing for walls
she says she will have to wait for some time before she will
be able to puncture that fresh new smoothness with nails to hang

her pictures up again   there is a row of crocheted carnations
around the book-shelf   and we admire her crocheted rag-rugs
scattered throughout the house   and encouraged she unfolds
a green-and-white one   oval   six by ten   made for a
                                            woman
in Ottawa   that's twenty-nine winter nights and days
cutting the materials and sixteen winter days and nights
crocheting the rug for five dollars   Mrs. Timm giggling now
is growing beautiful   made six last year for different ladies
that's thirty dollars   she has a moment of fear in her eyes
wondering if this joyous side-line is going to reduce
payments from the Department of Guess What Games We Play
"Charge them more, Mrs. Timm, way more," we say
knowing she does not know that we know where and how
these women live and how little five dollars is
in the accounting of their lives and how Mrs. Timm
is being robbed long distance without benefit of innocence
the seven birds who have flown are hung on the logs
beside this oval-framed picture of the strange young man
with the dark eyes and the lovely young girl at his side
with the eyes sharp as sparrows   how many selves ago
down the hall of mirrors into the silent chambers of disbelief
is this in the time of your life gone up the chimney
and down the road?   and we are her friends now
Mrs. Timm is growing beautiful and she invites us to see
the rest of the house   up-stairs to her cache of embroidery
and crochet   on the way up the steep narrow stairs
she picks up with a grin on her face the "sugar bowl"
stows it under the bed of another night without conveniences
two quilted beds in the rooms and one on the landing
Bethel the school-teacher's books line the log-cabin walls
and she opens a neat cupboard full of boxes tied with strings
and elastics and therein such a parade-day array of orange
and red and yellow pot-holders with scarlet tulips for trim
and doilies made of string and doilies made of No. 90
doilies made for all occasions coloured crocheted antimacassars
Crown of England doilies Star doilies The Queen Mary Doily
and what's this! a toaster cover!   how useful!   how brilliant!
oh, to be greeted on a dull desperate morning with this mardi gras
of roses around the insipid chrome of the dull pop-up toaster
mass-producing milled-out Weston's White   and towels
with crocheted borders and crocheted middles and crocheted
                                            bands

obviously towels not to be dried upon   "these are for when
I get my bathroom"   she is like a bride with a trousseau
a hope-chest   an infinite life-time stretched out
her eyes shine with a re-birth that will bring a flushing toilet
she presses upon us the pot-holders of our choice
we are now her friends   and she has no fear   this is her sign
of trust   I choose and carry them upwards on the palm of my
                                                                hand

a holy exchange   downstairs she says she has six orders
for rugs next winter—"If I last   If not, I tell Willie
I'll be hooking under the sod!   and Willie—he's so fond of his
                                                                pipe—
he says I'll know him under the sod by the little trail of smoke
creeping upwards—but I hope not for a long time"
Lord!   I have heard this woman's thesis   give her all the
                                                                degrees

Dariens are at the end of the last road at the last road's end
ewes with lambs and the woods are at the door-step
isolation is unlit   nothing has been said here
but face to face   in the winter the ice is water
and until the welfare workers came in and told Mother Darien
bride at sixteen about the baby bonuses if the children
went to school none of the thirteen went to school and some
of the older ones right now are out in the world of wilderness
without a letter or a number to their lives or livelihoods
and Saranna the sixteen-year-old when told she would go to
                                                                school
disappeared into the woods and has never been seen again
no worrying or searching   there is such an expectation of flight
they believe in survival   and all the little ones went right off
and collected Mother Darien's pay by attendance   the school
is a three-mile walk to the pick-up point where the school bus
loads them in half-frozen sometimes after the wait in January
six baloney sandwiches for each and a thermos of green tea
the miraculous e that makes the a say its own name   coloured
                                                                crayons
a teacher with nail polish and three coats   who would miss a
                                                                day?
and so the house when we enter it then is empty of all
adults   a backless chair   bench   table   cupboard
and two side-rooms off the stove where the kids sleep on
                                                                gunny-sacks

a little discontentedly now perhaps for they have been and seen
and wondered and made comparisons   in a great flurry of
                                        excitement
they give us seats   Papa Darien   Mother Darien and
                                         Margaret
and immediately Papa Darien tells us about his accident
shows us the sores all up his leg encrusted unhealed at 69
and how in the hospital they "treated him good, oh so good,
better than home"   such a gentle kind little lost Frenchman
sitting in his rocker by the stove worrying over his necessary foot
wondering if his three-score promised will allow him back
on his ninety acres   the unlettered unnumbered boy from
                                        Hamilton
has been summoned to return to his forefather's fields   the
                                        tyranny
of chores   the route to the room above is a cross between a
                                        ladder
and a stair   Margaret sits in the sun on the window-sill and
                                        laughs
her low guttural sensuous laugh   the bridled sexuality
"I'm twenty-eight now   I guess I'm an Old Maid
(won't somebody seen something down the road   say I'm
                                        not?)"

she moves like a cat to the cupboard   a recent trip to town
for welfare glasses has straightened her wall-eye   and we talk
about Man-Power Re-Training and the new classes for
                                        Illiterate Adults
how if she got to the road someone would pick her up
someone in phonetics at fifty   and she says she would surely
                                        like
to do that   read and write the way her little brothers and sisters
are doing now at the kitchen table by lamplight showing off
their learning   but the Old Man and the Old Woman make it
                                        clear
they do not want Margaret to go anywhere   do not want her to
                                        leave
do not want her to leave THEM   for here at the end of the road
this is what children are for at the end of the road
to care for the old people's old age   gratitude in duty
I WILL NOT ABIDE THIS USAGE OF THE CHILD AGED
                                        TWENTY-EIGHT

but bondage is always two-pronged two-sided multi-level
the imprisoner and the willingly imprisoned   Margaret
falls back now and says she would not leave her cows
her spinning   they clip their sheep and spin the wool
and knit the mitts and socks   Margaret proudly brings out
the beginning of next winter's hikes to the school
she hand-churns the butter and krauts down the cabbage
salts pork in the barrels and "Margaret Margaret are you grieving
over golden grove unleaving?"   Margaret Margaret has a
                                             mystery
a child by default to the virgin who waits
Beryl had a baby   Sister Beryl of the Busy Bushes
and wouldn't say if it was Tom, Dick or Harry's
and neither would the township keep it but turned Beryl loose
after signing the Baby Bonus forms of course homewards
down the road to "home is the place where when you go
they have to take you in"   but that tough beady-eyed one
Mother Darien—each flight always leaves at sixteen—
said "none of whore's brats in my house" and Beryl went down
                                             the road
to the third rise and left the baby on the grassy ditch there
crying to the heavens which fortunately was Margaret coming
                                             after
child in her arms and that slow angelic smile in the night
waking and smiling at the moon and the sleeping child
she stole food for it from the empty cupboards and the root-house
sent word with anyone who went that way to tell Beryl
to send money for the baby and when Mother Darien threatened
Margaret calmly said "I go also then"   and when still no word
came from the far world of Beryl of the Busy Bushes
Margaret forged the name on the baby bonuses and bought
for her foundling food clothes first toy and hugged him to her
                                             heart
so tight he never grew and now at five is still in diapers
and wets down his legs and speaks of nothing all the time
and stands sometimes in the barn-yard like an idiot
The used uses and abused abuses   at the hands of the jailer
I LEARNED THE ART OF JAILING   and Mother Darien
                                             serves us
green tea in chipped cups with a saucer for the special occasion
one of her unlettered and unnumbered sons has sent her
a radio for Christmas   and she says when the cheques come in

she could jump for joy on the side-walk but she doesn't
she bakes her own bread all the time   sometimes for supper
by lamplight the Dariens have hot bread, home-made butter and
                                                                  dills
and the children have never seen a doctor or a dentist
Papa Darien was let out of the hospital on condition
that he go back   he was so restless there they took pity on him
and let him go home for a few days   but he will not go back
the unlettered son who has leave of absence from his job
in Hamilton is returning to the city on Sunday
so Papa Darien there is no other way but out into the fields
this land never forgives a missed season   it over-runs
the man who is not daily obeisant   mornings and evenings
Darien is the name of the isthmus between two unfathomable
                                                                  oceans
and Margaret's window looks out on the arrogance
of missionaries, rescuers, educators

and the deaths that will break her open to the Twentieth Century.

W. P. KINSELLA

W. P. Kinsella's career as a writer of fiction began when he was in his early forties with the publication of Dance Me Outside *in 1977. This collection of stories about the Indian reserve near Hobbema in southern Alberta was the first of four books of Indian stories. In 1980 Kinsella turned to the fantastical possibilities of baseball with the stories in* Shoeless Joe Jackson Comes to Iowa, *and two years later he published the novel* Shoeless Joe, *which won the Houghton Mifflin Literary Fellowship in 1982 and the 1983* Books in Canada *first-novel award. "The Night Manny Mota Tied the Record" was one of a series of twelve new stories broadcast on* Anthology *and published in* Small Wonders *(CBC Enterprises, 1982). Penguin Books is publishing a new book of Kinsella's baseball stories,* The Thrill of the Grass, *in 1984. W. P. Kinsella taught for several years at the University of Calgary and now lives and writes full time in White Rock, near Vancouver.*

❖

The Night Manny Mota Tied
the Record

August 7, 1979: Dodger Stadium, Los Angeles, California. Dodgers are playing Houston Astros. I am seated high above the field, just to the third-base side of home plate. Pre-game presentations are being made. It is Mormon Family Night. The stadium is nearly full. It is five days since Thurman Munson died.

I spend my time people-watching. In front of me are a number of co-workers from an office of some kind, probably a food company, I decide, noting the size of the women. Every one of them is overweight, the one directly in front of me by about two hundred pounds. These women cram their sweating faces with every variety of concession food. The one in front of me has purchased a tray of six hotdogs. Several of them have whole trays of beer, six cups, each slopping foam over its waxy edge.

To my left, I watch an old man standing in the aisle staring at his ticket as if trying to decide where his seat should be. Eventually he chooses my aisle and makes his way to the seat next to me. He looks like a retired bank manager: iron-grey hair carefully styled, a blue pin-stripe suit, vest, and tie. He carries a zippered leather binder. What fascinates me is the ticket he holds in his left hand. As he stands in the aisle it appears to blink like a tiny computer making calculations. It flashes all the way down the row of seats, stopping as he slides into the chair next to mine.

Our eyes meet as he adjusts the small brown leather case in his lap, and I can see the same sense of tragedy floating in his eyes as I have viewed in my own the past five mornings.

"A terrible thing," I say.

He nods gravely. "Did you watch the funeral coverage on TV?"

It is my turn to nod. He has a sincere, fatherly voice that, my mind being preoccupied with the death of Thurman Munson, reminds me of the unseen baseball executive who talks to Munson in a widely shown commercial for a shaving product.

In the commercial, Munson knocks, then enters the executive's office, saying, "What's the problem? I'm playing good ball."

"You certainly are," the unseen executive says. "In my opinion, Thurman Munson is the finest catcher in the game."

As if reading my mind, the dapper old man beside me looks straight into my face and says, "Yes, a terrible loss, to the game and to the fans. In my opinion, Thurman Munson *is* the finest catcher in the game."

I feel like an egg with a finger-painted happy-face on it as I register my surprise.

"Is?" I say.

He leans towards me, smiling wryly, and speaks in a confidential manner. "Death," he says, "need not be as final as many of us are used to believing."

We are interrupted by the playing of the National Anthem. The old man stands at attention with his right hand over his heart. I look around me: everything appears to be normal, the palm trees beyond the left-field fence sway ever so slightly, reminding me of tiny ripples on an otherwise placid sea. I can discern nothing out of the ordinary except the presence next to me. When the anthem finishes I remain silent; whatever kind of game we are playing, it is his move.

"What would you say," the old man continues, "if I told you that it might just be possible to move time back, like a newsreel being played in reverse, and undo what has been done?" He stares at me, half smiling, giving me the chance to joke his statement away if I choose.

"You're talking about Thurman Munson?"

"More or less."

"Are you suggesting that if time were turned back, Munson's plane would have landed safely at the Canton Airport last week? That none of this would have happened?"

He nods.

"But at what price?" I say. "There has to be a catch."

"You're right, of course. As they say, there is no free lunch." He looks long at me, his kindly grey eyes on my face, and I'm sure at that instant we recognize each other for what we are, above and beyond business, family, or religion—baseball fans. The true word is fanciers. Fans of the game itself. Men having favourites, but not blind prejudices, here because we love the game. Not Sunday fathers dragging young sons after us, or college kids guzzling beer and cheering ourselves hoarse, but steady, long-term, win-or-lose fans. I can tell by looking at him that he has seen Mike Marshall work on a sleety April night in Bloomington; that he has endured the arctic cross-winds of Candlestick Park in San Francisco and Exhibition Stadium in Toronto; that he has been jellied in his seat by the steam-cabinet humidity of Busch Stadium in August. I feel towards that old man the camaraderie that soldiers must feel for their fellows as they travel home after a long campaign.

"My name is Revere," he says, extending a manicured hand that is solid as a ham, a baseball player's hand. "I caught a little myself at one time," he says, knowing I can feel the outsize fingers, like plump, scarred sausage. "I think we should have a serious talk."

"The price," I say. "What is the price of tampering with time?"

The game had begun. Jerry Reuss, pitching for the Dodgers, set Houston down in the first without a murmur.

"I'll explain the situation to you exactly as it is. No deception. I'll always be candid with you. Don't feel badly if you don't believe me. In fact, most people don't."

"Go on," I say.

He talks for a full inning. Explaining to me as if I were a child attending his first baseball game and he were a benevolent grandfather outlining the rules between hotdogs and orange drinks.

"What you're saying is. . ." but I am interrupted by the rising roar of the crowd as Joe Ferguson of the Dodgers strokes a home run to right field. I was not involved with what was happening and have to stare around the buffalo-like woman in front of me to see if there are runners on base. Revere and I applaud politely, sit down while the people around us are still standing; it is like sliding into the shade of a fence on a summer's day. As the buzz of the crowd subsides I continue:

"What you're saying is that everyone has someone, somewhere, who, if contacted and agreeable, could replace them in death."

"Badly put but basically accurate," says Mr. Revere. "Limited, of course, to people who have achieved fame or made an outstanding contribution to society, and who still have an outstanding contribution left to make if given a second chance."

"And you're suggesting to me that I might be able to sacrifice myself in order to give Thurman Munson a longer life."

"At this point I am only acquainting you with the situation. I want to make that very clear. There are many of us at locations throughout the world. Our search is rather like a game: we have a few days to find the one person in the world who can, if he or she desires, make the event—in this case Thurman Munson's death—unhappen, so to speak. Experience teaches us that the natural places to be looking are ballparks, taverns, and assembly lines..."

"My case would be a little different," I say. "It would be like a chain of command, if I replaced Munson, why, there would be someone out there who could, if you found him, replace me."

"I'm afraid I don't understand," Mr. Revere says, looking genuinely puzzled.

I introduce myself. "I'm a writer," I say. "I've published four books. Have dozens left to write."

"Really?"

"Short stories, too. Over a hundred of them. I've had very good reviews."

"It's embarrassing," Mr. Revere says, "but I would have known if you were on the protected list. Something we never do is ask one protected person to replace another. And it isn't like we didn't know your name. We have ways of knowing things like that," and he taps the side pocket of his suit where he had deposited what may or may not have been a ticket stub that winked and blinked.

"But I'm relatively famous," I protest. "I've made a contribution. I'm at least well known." Mr. Revere remains silent. "I *do* have a following."

"I'm sure you do. But you must understand, our list is small. Few writers." He smiles as if reminiscing. "Hemingway was there."

"But you couldn't find his..."

"Oh, but we did. Even as a young man he contemplated suicide. Used his service revolver one night. There was a retired bullfighter who replaced him."

Houston goes scoreless in the third. There are a couple of hits but I scarcely notice. Usually I keep a score card. Use a green or purple felt pen and have the card woven over with patterns as if it were a square of afghan. Tonight my program lies whitely on my knee.

"If you're totally appalled at the idea, you must let me know," says Mr. Revere. "If you feel that I'm senile, or crazy, or if you know that you could never do such a thing, don't take up my time. There was a certain magic about you or I wouldn't be here."

Thurman Munson: I have never been a fan of his, though I recognized his greatness. It was the Yankees. They have always been like the rich kid on the block who could afford real baseballs and a bat that wasn't cracked. You played him, you tolerated him, but you were never sorry when he got spiked.

"No," I hear myself saying, "tell me more. Still, dying. . ."

"Ceasing to exist," corrects Mr. Revere.

"Dying," I insist. "Euphemisms don't change the nature of the beast. It is definitely, ah, quite final?" I ask.

"I'm afraid it would be, as we say, terminal."

Mr. Revere settles back to watch the game, a rather sly smile playing at the corners of his mouth.

Ferguson and Yeager hit back-to-back homers for the Dodgers in the fourth. The fans in front of us, whom I have mentally named the Buffalo Brigade, all stand, blocking my vision. The largest woman has made two trips to the concession since the game started. She applauds with half a hotdog protruding obscenely from her mouth. I remain in my seat as each of the home-run hitters circles the bases.

Die. The word rings through me as if it were a bolt rattling in my hollow metal interior. Whom would I die for? My wife? I like to think that we are beyond that kind of emotional self-sacrifice. I would, in a split-second situation, endanger myself, say, to push her from the path of a speeding car, but, given a thoughtful choice like this, of quietly dying so the other might live, I suspect we might each choose to save ourselves. My daughters? Yes. In effect I would be saving my own life by saving them. My grandchildren? The blood ties thin. I think not. Is there anyone else? I have never had a friend for whom I would even consider such a sacrifice. A stranger? As unlikely as it seems, there are probably several.

I look over at Mr. Revere; he appears engrossed in the game. "Take your time," he says, still looking at the emerald infield. "Feel free to ask questions."

What would motivate someone to make the supreme sacrifice so that a stranger might live? Heroism is the only word I can muster. Heroism, I believe, is something basic to human nature. I have often fantasized delivering my wife or daughters from some holocaust, or walking steely-eyed into the jaws of death to rescue one or more of them, perhaps, afterwards, expiring in their grateful arms, my mission accomplished, the cheers of the crowd fading slowly as my life ebbed.

An idea begins to form. I inch forward on my seat.

"I'm afraid not," Mr. Revere says. I look at him harshly.

"Couldn't I rescue him from the plane?" I suggest.

I could see myself racing across the tarmac of that airport near Canton, Ohio, tearing open the door of the plane and dragging Thurman Munson's body to safety, gripping him under the arms like a two-hundred-and-twenty-five-pound sack of flour and backing away from the flaming wreckage. Later, when I was interviewed by television and newspaper reporters, I would speak modestly of my accomplishment, displaying my bandaged hands. I would be known as The Man Who Rescued Thurman Munson.

"Our operatives are always quite anonymous," says Mr. Revere.

"No possibility of recognition. It makes the choice harder," I say.

"It eliminates the insincere," says Mr. Revere, returning his attention to the game.

I am silent for a few moments. "What would happen to me?" I say to Mr. Revere's neatly trimmed, white, right sideburn. He is intent on the game; Houston has a bit of a rally going.

"You needn't have any fear of pain," he replies, sounding, I think, suspiciously like a dentist. "You might, after the game, decide to sleep for a few moments in your car before driving home. It would be peaceful, like sinking into a warm vat of pink cotton batting."

"What guarantee do I have?"

"None at all. You would have to sense that I'm telling the truth. You would have to feel the magic, see the world from a slightly different angle, like batting while lying prone."

"Whom have you saved? How many?"

"Not as many as we'd like. Our business can be compared to searching for the proverbial needle in the haystack. We have many more failures than successes. The rather sad fact is that no one ever hears of our successes."

"Who?" I insist. "Name names."

He unzippers the leather binder in his lap and produces a front page from the *New York Times*. The headline reads: PRESIDENT FORD ASSASSINATED IN SACRAMENTO. Below it is a large photograph of Squeaky Fromme holding a smoking gun.

"We went through four hectic days in nineteen-seventy-five, the days after Miss Fromme's gun didn't misfire. Gerald Ford's body was lying in state in Washington when we found the party."

"Of course, there is no way to verify that!"

"Absolutely none." Enos Cabell ends the Astros' fifth, but not before they score two runs to cut the Dodger lead to four-two.

"What about John Kennedy?" I cry. "Half the world would have given their lives for him. I would have. Still would..."

"There is only one chance for each person on our list. We saved him once, during the PT-one-oh-nine sinking. It was a young black woman from Memphis who..." and his voice trails off.

I think about Thurman Munson, remember how I heard of his death. I didn't listen to TV or radio the night of August second. Mornings I write. My wife, who teaches at a nearby university, brings a newspaper home at lunchtime. On August third she brought me ice cream to soften the blow. When I'm troubled or disturbed or can't write, I often head for the nearest Baskin-Robbins. At noon on August third, my wife walked into my study without knocking and handed me a cardboard cup overflowing with chocolate and coconut ice cream, my favourites. There was a fuchsia-coloured plastic spoon stabbed into the middle of it.

"There's bad news in the paper," she said.

"Did the Twins lose again?" I replied.

"I'm serious," she added.

I was going to say, "So am I," but didn't as I caught the serious inflection in her voice.

"Bobby Kennedy?" I say to Mr. Revere. "Martin Luther King?"

The Houston Astros, as ragtag a crew of ballplayers as ever held first place in August, are running wild in the sixth inning, forcing errors, blooping hits, stealing bases. In front of us, the Buffalo Brigade are shuffling in and out with new armloads of food. It is very difficult for two fat people to pass in the narrow space between rows.

"We should be thankful they are sitting in front of us rather than behind," says Mr. Revere. "If one of them should fall forward, I'm afraid it could be fatal."

I repeat my previous question.

"We were unable to find the party representing Dr. King."

"Then he's still out there. You could still..."

"We have only a short period. Even now the time for Mr. Munson runs low. We did find the man representing Robert Kennedy. In fact I found him myself. He was an Eastern philosopher, a man of great religious piety. He refused to cooperate. He had no qualms about his own fate, but his belief was that death is the highest attainable state; therefore he felt it would be a tremendous disservice to bring any man back to this world after he had experienced the next."

"How do the people feel who come back?"

"They never know they've been away," Mr. Revere says. "Gerald Ford thinks that Miss Fromme's gun misfired. Hemingway thought he changed his mind about suicide in nineteen-eighteen. We are able to be of service sometimes, but our odds of success are rather like hitting eighteen in blackjack. Not very high."

"Who is the 'We' you keep referring to? You make it sound like a corporation. Who are you?"

"Perhaps we should watch the baseball game for a while," suggests Mr. Revere, smiling kindly.

I look at the scoreboard. The Astros have put up six runs in the sixth inning with my hardly noticing, and now lead eight-four.

I wonder about Thurman Munson. Would he want to come back? I picture Thurman Munson dead, his spine splintered like a bat hit on the trademark. Tentative cause of death, asphyxiation, caused by breathing in toxic chemicals from the burning craft. I understand now why I couldn't be rescuer, why his friends couldn't move his body from the wreckage. His spine shattered; he wouldn't have wanted to be rescued. Would he want to come back now? For all his short life he did what he loved best. He died with the smell of the grass still in his nostrils. The crack of the bat and the rising roar of the crowd never had to fade away and become muted memories like distant thunder. He never lived to hear some fresh kid say, "Who was Thurman Munson?" He left a beautiful wife and a young family he loved very much. I suppose that would be the best argument for granting him a second chance, and I recall a picture in the newspaper of his young son, Michael, wearing a baseball uniform with Munson's number fifteen, and the story of his asking why everyone was sad and saying that they should be happy that Munson was with God. "God has taken Daddy to heaven because He needs good people there."

Still, I wonder, would that be such a bad way to remember your father...having him taken when you were still young enough not to realize that he was only a very ordinary mortal?

Some athletes can't adjust to retirement; relationships disintegrate. There are many old baseball players who sell cars or insurance, drink too much, and wish that they had gone out in their prime while they were still adored by the fans. I recall the emotionally exhausting scene at Yankee Stadium as the crowd cheered for nine minutes when Thurman Munson's picture was flashed on the scoreboard. Many fans, tears streaming down their cheeks, cheered themselves into exhaustion, somewhat exorcising the grief that hung in their chests like concrete.

Perhaps, I consider, no one is meant to tamper with time.

I try to concentrate on the game but can't.

"There is magic," Mr. Revere says. "It is close by. I can tell when someone feels it."

"It is the game," I say. "Not you."

"We all have to claim some game as magic," he says and takes from the inside pocket of his jacket a thick sheaf of paper that looks like a half-dozen sheets of foolscap folded over. I strain to get a look at what is written on them. I can't distinguish the letterhead, but there appears to be long lists of questions with little boxes after each, places for Mr. Revere to make X's or check marks.

"Name?" and he reads my full name for me to verify. "A writer, you say. I'm afraid I haven't read anything of yours. My job keeps me quite busy, as you can imagine."

During the next inning Mr. Revere plies me with more irrelevant questions than a tax return and loan application combined. There are questions about ancestry, employment, family, hobbies; it is as though I am being interviewed by a very thorough reporter. I am reminded that I once underwent, in connection with an employment application, the MMPI (Minnesota Multiphasic Personality Inventory), a series of several hundred questions designed to supply a detailed personality profile. Mr. Revere's questions are equally probing but do not include such MMPI gems as: *Are you a messenger of God?* and *Has your pet died recently?*

As I answer the questions my mind is working at three levels, with the baseball game being relegated to the lowest, Mr. Revere's questions to the second level, while my top priority becomes: What will I do if I am chosen?

I am forty-eight years old; I am not ready to die.

"Thurman Munson was only thirty-two and he wasn't ready to die either," says Mr. Revere between questions.

In my time, given this opportunity, whom would I die for? The names flash past me like calendar pages blown in the wind: FDR, Dr. Tom Dooley, Bobby Greenlease, Perry Smith, Bogart, Jim Reeves, Elvis, Lyman Bostock, Martin Luther King, Gandhi, James Dean, Amelia Earhart, Lou Gehrig...

"Given the choice, would you rather be an aeronautical engineer, a sign painter, or a dishwasher?"

My head feels as though a dealer is shuffling cards inside it, his thumbs have slipped, and I'm inundated in an avalanche of playing cards. "What on earth do you care for? I have zero mechanical ability. I can't draw. I would rather be a dishwasher."

"I'm sorry," Mr. Revere says, giving me his grandfatherly smile. "Everything used to be much simpler. We are experimenting with some rather advanced concepts in hopes of increasing our success rate. I'm sure you understand."

I recall Sidney Carton's words from *A Tale of Two Cities*, something to the effect that " 'Tis a far, far better thing I do than ever I have done before." It is only the hero complex again, rising out of the crowd in front of me like the Loch Ness monster.

"Why me?" I almost shout, causing several people to glance my way briefly, annoyed that I have distracted them from the excitement of a Dodger rally in the eighth.

"Because you love the game for the sake of the game. There aren't many of us left. It is rather like finding a genuinely religious person..."

"I'm not exactly unprejudiced," I say. "To put it mildly, I have never been a Yankee fan. I resent a team that buys its winning percentage."

"You disapprove of the management, but do you hate the players?"

"Hate is a word that has no place in sports. I've never cheered for Thurman Munson, except in all-star games, but I don't hang over railings with a red face and hair in my eyes screaming insults either."

"And you stay until the last out, even if one team is winning twelve-zero." I nod. But the question remains: What will I do if he chooses me? I feel like the thirteenth at table. A chance to be either a god or a devil.

The crowd suddenly breaks into a chant: "Manny! Manny! Manny!" Rhythmic, ritualistic, the voice of the crowd rises like a monstrous choir as the leather-faced veteran Manny Mota appears from the dugout to swing his bat in the on-deck circle.

Manny Mota has one hundred and forty-three pinch hits in his career and needs one to tie and two to break the record held by Smoky Burgess.

"Manny! Manny! Manny!" the crowd rhapsodizes as he approaches the plate.

The largest of the Buffalo Brigade, built to resemble a chest of drawers with an encyclopaedia set on top of it, stunned by copious amounts of beer, remains standing even after Mota has stepped into the batter's box, completely blocking my view. Shouts of "Down in front" come from other people whose view is also obstructed. She ignores the shouts, if she hears them. She stands sturdy and dark as a pillar, a container of beer raised in her cupcake hand; I see her as the bloated corpse of the Statue of Liberty.

On a two-strike count Mota slashes a hard grounder to the right side. Landestoy, the Houston second baseman, gets in front of it, but the force of the ball turns him around. He regains his balance and fires to first but the split-second delay was all Mota needed: he is safe on a very close play. The fans roar their approval. Mota tips his hat to the crowd. When he is replaced by a pinch runner the crowd stands again to cheer him back to the dugout.

Mr. Revere, apparently through with his interrogation, folds the legal-size pages of questions and, unzipping his leather binder, places them carefully in the bottom between what look like sheets of cardboard or black plastic that may have been blinking golden like a night sky.

The briefcase seems to be making a whirring sound as if thousands and thousands of tiny impulses are perhaps processing the information just fed to it.

I look around at the ecstatic crowd. I look at the fat lady, still standing.

"I've decided to do it," I say to Mr. Revere.

"I know," and he smiles in his most kindly manner and I somehow picture a sweet-pea- and petunia-scented evening on the veranda of a square, white, two-storey house somewhere in Middle America where a grandfather and a child sit in the luminous dusk and talk of baseball and love and living. A feeling of comfort surrounds and calms me and I feel an all-encompassing love for my fellow man, so strong that I must be experiencing what others who have found religious faith have experienced. I love all mankind. I love the fat lady.

Mr. Revere reopens his zippered case and takes out the questionnaire. He studies it closely. I recognize that it is subtly different but I cannot say how. Perhaps only my perceptions are different.

Mr. Revere smiles again, a smile of infinite sadness, and patience and love. "I'm sorry," he says. "You're not the one."

"But I've decided," I say.

"I'm aware of that. I appreciate...we appreciate that you want to help. I'm afraid I may have spoiled a very good ballgame for you..."

"But I want to..." my voice rises like a whining child's.

"I'm sorry." Mr. Revere is extending his hand to me.

"I'm not good enough," I flare. People are staring at me. The ballpark is very quiet. Houston is batting in the ninth, going out with a whimper. "I warn you, I'm a writer. I intend to write about this."

"Suit yourself," says Mr. Revere calmly. "In fact, feel free. If we find the right party in the next few days, everything that transpired tonight will be obliterated from every memory. But if we don't..." he smiles again. "Why, who would believe you? If someone actually tracked me down, I'd plead innocence or senility or both. I'm just a retired gentleman from Iowa who came to Los Angeles for a few baseball games and sat beside a strange and rather disturbed young man. You'd end up looking rather foolish, I suspect. Anyway, no one should believe a silly old man who goes around baseball stadiums talking about resurrecting the dead," and he chuckles.

The game ends. Mr. Revere makes his way briskly to the aisle and disappears in the crowd. I eventually edge my way to the aisle and down the steps for ten or fifteen rows. The Buffalo Brigade are now behind me. I turn to look at them. I scrunch myself against the railing and wait for them to catch up with me. There is something I have to know.

The fat lady huffs down the stairs towards me. I turn and face her in all her grossness. Her forehead and cheeks are blotched and somewhat out of focus, as though her face is covered by an inch or two of water.

"It was you I was going to do it for," I say. The fat lady stops in mid-waddle, puffs her cheeks like a child, and belches. "It was you that Manny Mota made the hit for. If you'd only realize it. Why don't you realize it?" I stand in the middle of the aisle facing up towards her. She is close enough for her sweetish odours of beer and perspiration to envelop me.

"Are you all right, fella?" a man behind her directs the words my way.

"Move along," somebody else shouts.

"Thurman Munson died for you," I say to the fat lady, who, three steps above me, glares down in bloodshot indignation.

"Oh, Jesus," says a voice behind her, a voice that is somewhere between an oath and a prayer.

GWENDOLYN MACEWEN

Gwendolyn MacEwen has been a writer ever since she left school at eighteen, and for much of that time she has been a frequent contributor to CBC radio programs. She is a fine poetry reader and has read much of her own work and the work of other poets on Anthology *and other programs. She has written verse drama for radio and the libretto for "Carnival", a jazz composition by Ron Collier.*

Gwendolyn MacEwen is the author of two novels, books for children, travel recollections about Greece, a collection of short stories, Noman *(to be re-issued in 1984 with a new collection of her short fiction), and almost a dozen books of poetry. She won a Governor General's Award for poetry in 1969 for* The Shadow-Maker. *She read from the manuscript of* The T. E. Lawrence Poems *on* Anthology *in 1982, and the book itself was published later that year by Mosaic Press. The poems that follow are taken from that book.*

❀

The Desert

Only God lives there in the seductive Nothing
That implodes into pure light. English makes Him
    an ugly monosyllable, but Allah breathes
A fiery music from His tongue, ignites the sands,
    invents a terrible love that is
The very name of pain.

The desert preserves Him
    as the prophets found Him, massive and alone.
They went there, into that awful Zero
        to interpret Him,
    for Himself to know, for He said: Help me,

I am the One who is alone, not you. Tell Me who I am.

Camels lean into the desert, lost in some thought
                     so profound it can only be guessed. When
Will God invent man? When
                               will the great dream end?
My skin crawls with a horrible beauty in this
                    Nothingness, this Everything—

I fall to my knees in the deep white sand, and my head
                    implodes into pure light.

The Absolute Room

We came to a place which was the centre of ourselves
                    in the desert between Aleppo and Hama;
We came to this Roman place where a hundred scents
                    were built somehow right into the walls.
So the old man and the boy led us through courts
                    of jasmine, and many other flowers, then

Into this great hall where all the scents slayed
                    each other, and were still, and all
We breathed was pure desert air.

                              We call
                this room the sweetest of them all,
You said.
                And I thought: *Because there is nothing here.*

I knew then that you possessed nothing of me, and I
                    possessed nothing of you, Dahoum.
We were wealthy and stuffed with a wondrous nothing
                    that filled the room and everything around.

You looked into my eyes, the windows to my soul,
      and said that because they were blue
You could see right through them, holes in my skull,
      to the quiet, powerful sky beyond.

A Farewell to Carcemish

Time contains me as once your eyes contained me, utterly.

I leave you to guard the site,
                          its layers of history.
I am moving back to the world,
                            I exit sideways, slide
From your eyes.
                 No one is with you. The sightless desert
Is with you.
              Wind from the sun
                         stirs your black robes.
Maktub: It is written.

He is only dangerous who dreams by day.

Horses

Horses. Horses of the dawn,
Shadowy horses, dreaming horses,
Parallel horses, horses at right angles,
Horses of the afternoon and horses of the evening,

Horses who were the custodians of our souls
And kept our mad desires in check—
Bloody horses, stolen horses, gift horses, fallen horses—
I have ridden them all, beasts
                   of the most exalted sun.

Their ghosts are here now; they are
        horses of heaven;
They speak to me of midnight and the last dark wadi.

Solar Wind

It comes upon you unawares—
        something racing out of the edge
Of your vision, as when you are staring at something
    and not staring—looking through—
A herd of white horses grazing on the periphery
Of your sight, and the afternoon
        slanting into night—

Comes the wind that is
      the colour of the sun, and your eyes
    which are nuggets of gold follow it
    down the barrels of the rifles, through
    the gun-cotton, and over the culverts,
Leaving everything gold, gold in its wake.

The past and the future are burning up; the present
    melts down the middle, a river of wind,
    wind from the sun, gold wind, anything—
And suddenly you know that all mysteries have been solved
    for you, all questions answered.

You must find a god to worship or you will die
In that unholy moment just before darkness and the sound
Of guns.

CHARLES RITCHIE

The critic George Woodcock has said of Charles Ritchie's The Siren Years
*that this book of memoirs of London during the Second World War "provided
the first evidence that from the rich experience of a Canadian public servant,
literature could be created." Charles Ritchie had a distinguished career in the
Canadian diplomatic service and now lives in retirement in Ottawa and Nova
Scotia.* The Siren Years *immediately established him in a second career as a
brilliant diarist of our times, and won a Governor General's Award for 1974.
It was followed by three more memoirs,* An Appetite for Life, *Diplomatic* Passport, *and* Storm Signals *(Macmillan).*

*"My Cousin Gerald" won the first award for a memoir in the CBC literary
competition in 1979. It appears here in print for the first time.*

❖

My Cousin Gerald

I cannot remember a time when I do not remember my cousin
Gerald. He was the son of my mother's elder sister, Geraldine, a
pretty, spirited girl who died at the age of eighteen in giving birth
to him. She had married Arthur Branscombe, an officer in the
British Army, stationed in Halifax, Nova Scotia, who after her
death followed his military career in various outposts of the empire,
leaving Gerald to be brought up by his English relations among
whom he was shuttled about like a misdirected parcel. An excitable,
high-strung child, he was made to feel that it was a bore having
him about, and that was the beginning of his becoming himself a
bore. Unloved, he was clamorous for attention; unlistened to, he
talked incessantly. From India, from Malta, from Mauritius, came
admonitory letters from his father. On his visits home he took the
boy out to lunch. These were landmarks in Gerald's life. He felt he
had a right to love his father, but his father found him a son of
whom he could not be proud. Reports from the second-rate public
school to which he had been consigned spoke of his sloppiness and
his "inability to stick to anything". Colonel Branscombe detested
sloppiness and had always been able to stick to one thing—himself.

He was a balloon of a man, priding himself on being the fattest man in the British Army. He had tiny hands and tiny feet encased in immaculately polished boots and his moustache was waxed to a fine point. He had wit and a stock of selfish charm. His military career was moderately successful, but his later years were darkened by a miscalculation. Having commuted his military pension for cash, he married as his second wife a commonplace woman of means whom he counted on to support his old age in comfort. She, for her part, had married him counting on playing the Colonel's Lady. Both were disappointed. Within a year of his marriage he retired from the army. They went to live in Cheltenham, where she kept him on a stringent allowance—barely enough, he complained, to pay for his pre-luncheon pink gin at the club.

Years earlier he had been in love with my mother. It was in the days when it was illegal to marry one's deceased wife's sister. I have seen the poems that he wrote to her, bemoaning this barrier to their union. In fact, she never contemplated him as a husband, but she had an indulgent fondness for him. It was at this time, when she was still a young woman, that she was first moved by compassion for Gerald, then an acne-stricken adolescent in awe of his father and unable to please him. Her compassion, laced with irritation, was to last a lifetime. Gerald had just conspicuously failed his entrance examination for Oxford and already showed promise of becoming one of life's casualties. My mother suggested that he might do better in Canada, and Colonel Branscombe welcomed the suggestion with enthusiasm.

From then on, year in and year out, my mother applied her considerable energy and ingenuity to finding jobs for Gerald. As soon as she found him one, he lost it. There was a touch of the poltergeist about Gerald. When he was roped with fellow members of a surveyors' team in the Rocky Mountains, his foot slipped and he brought his team-mates crashing down after him. While he escaped harm himself, two of his companions were badly injured. Employed as a post-office letter sorter, he generated chaos. When he was cutting wood on a farm, the blade of his axe flew from the handle and cut the farmer's foot so badly that he had to have his toes amputated.

The First World War interrupted Gerald's attempts to earn a living. He at once joined up as a private and served in France. In the army he was looked upon as something between a joke and a regimental mascot. His Colonel admitted to relief when he was invalided out suffering from shell-shock. "A plucky little fellow," he commented, "but no addition to the war effort."

It was on Gerald's return to Nova Scotia after the war that he became, as my mother put it, "part of our lives"—a part which my brother and I, then young, could have well dispensed with. He must at this time have been about thirty years old, but seemed of no known age; rather to be a superannuated schoolboy. He was small and plump, with a perennially red round face and protruding blue eyes. For some reason which baffled and infuriated my mother, his clothes appeared always to be several sizes too large for him, as though bought under the impression that he was a much bigger man than he was. His coat sleeves used to cover his hands nearly to his finger ends.

He was usually intermittently employed, but his real life was lived in the local amateur dramatic society. Since childhood he had had a passion for the stage. It was a passion which unfortunately was not to be requited, for he could never quite bridge the gulf that separates the amateur from the professional. I remember our embarrassment when we loyally used to attend his performances. He specialized in the song-and-dance acts of the period. As Burlington Bertie or as the Colonel of the Nuts, he cavorted before a chorus, twirling a cane, with a silk hat or a boater cocked over one eye.

Gerald used to come to lunch with us on Sundays at our home in Nova Scotia. It was with sinking hearts that we heard his voice hallooing cheerily in the hall. He always came early, hurrying up the drive to the house and on arrival sweating profusely from his exertions. Torn from our Sunday morning inertia, we braced ourselves for the encounter. Gerald's conversation was a merciless monologue. Directly we sat down to the table, we would be plunged into the intrigues and counter-intrigues, the outrages and rivalries, of amateur theatricals. "Lola," Gerald said of the lady who directed the local company, "was exceedingly rude about my performance. Of course, it is all jealousy on her part and she knows nothing about the theatre. I felt it would be beneath me to argue with her, so I just snapped my fingers under her nose"—here he mimed the scene, snapping his fingers with an audible crack—"and I walked off the stage." "That was an extremely silly thing to do," my mother remarked. "Oh, no, Aunt Lilian! Cyril didn't think so. Cyril backed me up completely. He thinks my act the best part of the show and after all, he is almost a professional actor." "I wish," said my mother, "that you would stop hanging about that young man Cyril." Gerald was an inordinately slow eater, whereas my mother was an exceptionally fast one. As lunch stretched on interminably while he talked and masticated she would lose patience and cry, "Do eat up, Gerald, for goodness' sake."

After lunch, my brother and I took turns on alternate Sundays going for a walk with Gerald. It was a trying experience. We were boys at an age when behaviour attracting public attention is particularly mortifying. Gerald had a habit of taking off his hat to any passers-by on the street and addressing a polite "Good afternoon" to them as if he were a public figure, perhaps the Prince of Wales bestowing a greeting on his subjects. The passers-by did not recognize him as the Prince of Wales but they sensed his oddity and his patronage. Some mumbled a mistrustful reply. Others hurried on, casting an irritated look at him. If asked, "Do you know that person?" Gerald would reply, "Many people know me whom I do not know."

We were sometimes tempted to disavow our relationship with him when some boy or girl of our own age who had seen us with him asked, "Who was that funny little man with the English accent?" But my mother would not put up with such weakness. "Blood is thicker than water. Gerald is your cousin and I hope you boys are not so feeble as to pay any attention to what other people say about him. If he had inherited the baronetcy (there was a vague baronetcy in Gerald's family) and was living in a big house, people would say he was mildly eccentric and would be delighted to accept his hospitality. It is just that he can't cope with earning his own living and he doesn't fit in anywhere. Poor Gerald."

Finally, Gerald saved up enough money to go to New York to try his fortunes on the stage. It was only when he had trailed from audition to audition, from hope to disappointment, that he returned home. Something else marked his time in New York, something hinted at but never recounted by him. It was, I think, some sexual misadventure; perhaps, as in matters theatrical, he could not distinguish between the amateur and the professional, and was unable to cope with the latter.

Even after his New York disillusionment, Gerald continued to haunt the local theatre in Halifax, hoping for walking-on parts with visiting touring companies. When the romantic actor Sir John Martin Harvey came to town playing in *The Only Way*, the adaptation of Dickens' *Tale of Two Cities*, Gerald pestered to join the French revolutionary mob, but was instead given the job of raising and letting fall the curtain. My brother and I were in the audience on the opening night. Martin Harvey, in the role of Sidney Carton, was delivering his dying words from the foot of the guillotine: "It is a far, far better thing that I do today than I have ever done before." Half-way through his speech, the curtain clattered down, and then after a pause of a minute or two, was run up again in a halting and unsteady fashion, revealing Martin Harvey looking deeply vexed still at the foot of the guillotine. "It's Gerald again," my brother hissed at me. "I know," I replied.

In the autumn of 1929 my mother went for her annual visit to England, where I was then an undergraduate at Oxford. At the same time Gerald had come to England to settle his father's estate, for Colonel Branscombe had died of boredom in Cheltenham. His estate consisted mainly of several handsomely bound volumes of Napier's *Peninsular War* (one volume missing), and a monumental silver inkstand inscribed with the names of his old companions in the regiment. There was no money. The widow gave Gerald a sparse welcome. "She did not even offer me a cup of tea. She said that my father had left a letter addressed to me, but that she must have mislaid it when cleaning out his desk, and if she found it, she would send it on to me."

My mother, while in England, was in the habit of having a small sherry party each year for the purpose of "polishing off" some of her acquaintances. More interesting or intimate friends were not included—this was a settling of petty social accounts. That year it took place in the Hyde Park Hotel. The guests had at one time or another served in Halifax, either in the garrison or with the fleet. They were elderly people for the most part, and conversation played over reminiscences of the old days. Sherry was for the ladies and for the gentlemen also, unless they took a firm stand in favour of something stronger, when whiskey could be produced from behind a screen. The hotel waiters were dispensed with as my brother and myself handed around the drinks. This arrangement made the gathering more informal and, incidentally, cheaper.

The party, if not in full swing, was trundling along quite amiably when Gerald arrived. He had borrowed or hired for the occasion a dark-blue suit which hung in folds about him. On his feet were boots so much too big for him that he appeared to be walking on snowshoes, which he had difficulty in controlling as he crossed the parquet floor of the hotel drawing-room. His manner was eager but agitated. My mother swept him with a look of irritated resignation. "This is my nephew, Gerald," she introduced. "You remember my sister Geraldine." "Indeed yes," cooed Lady Hoskins, the doyenne of the party. "I knew your dear mother so well.

Come sit down beside me." Gerald obeyed and without delay burst into one of his non-stop monologues. His eyes seemed to be almost popping out of his head with excitement at whatever he was telling Lady Hoskins. I glanced at him uneasily. The muted general conversation was continuing when it was arrested by a burst of song, loud and unexpected. Gerald had sprung to his feet and was giving a spirited rendering of one of his favourite numbers:

"I'm Burlington Bertie, I rise at 10:30,
I walk down the Strand with my gloves in my hand,
And I walk up again with them off.
I've just had a banana with Lady Diana,
I'm Burlington Bertie from Bow."

As he sang, he twirled an imaginary cane, cocked an invisible straw hat and waved a pair of real gloves which he produced like a conjurer from his pocket. Gaily he capered into the middle of the room. He was not drunk. He had hardly touched his sherry glass. My mother fixed him with a compelling eye. "Gerald," she said. "Would you pass the olives to Mrs. Stormley." Abandoning his act, he quietly proceeded to Mrs. Stormley's side. Major Unwin, an old stalwart, who had rated a whiskey, called across the room to him, "I say, what a performance! You should be on the stage." A blush of pleasure reddened Gerald's face, and he cast down his eyes demurely. There was a faint murmur of congratulations from the ladies, who seemed uncertain as to whether or not my mother had planned this divertissement to liven up the part.

A few minutes later there was a rustle of impending departure. Gerald now rose to his feet, yawned in an affected manner and called out to my mother in a carrying, stagey voice: "Did I tell you, Aunt Lilian, that I caught syphilis last Wednesday." "That is not at all funny," she replied in a controlled voice. "Just sit down, dear." Gerald sat. The room had been momentarily shocked into silence, people turned to stone where they stood. Then the ladies began to move toward the door, taking leave of my mother with airs of stricken condolence. They made no mention of what they could hardly believe they had heard. Only Major Unwin muttered to me in a farewell aside: "Quite a character, your cousin Gerald."

After the incident at the sherry party, there was a change in Gerald. His ebullience seemed to have subsided. He would fall into long spells of silent gloom, and had taken to talking to himself. My mother had rented a house in the country not far from Oxford, and there he came to stay with us for Christmas. On Christmas night we had a small party with crackers, paper hats and champagne. Gerald sat at the table rolling his eyes apprehensively, and as usual munching his food long after the rest of us had finished. From time to time he made pathetic efforts to simulate gaiety, and once attempted a song. After dinner my brother, dressed up as Father Christmas with a white cotton beard, came into the room to distribute some presents. When he approached him with a parcel in his hand, Gerald backed away from him, gazing in terror at the beard, and covered his face with his hands.

Our neighbours in the country, Lord and Lady C., had been kind enough to say that we could use their park. One day after Christmas, Gerald and I were walking there when I saw approaching us the rather forbidding figure of Lord C., a stout man with a walrus moustache. Suddenly Gerald raced towards him and thrust his arms around the astonished land-owner, crying "Father, Father."

When one has always been used to the company of an eccentric person, one is slow to notice the shift from oddity to insanity. My mother, always protective toward Gerald, was reluctant to face the change in him. Yet, in the following weeks she began to consult mental specialists. They were infuriatingly indecisive about the nature of his illness, whether it was mind or body or both. All agreed, however, that he had never contracted syphilis. Meanwhile his condition became rapidly worse. He began to hear voices and, in particular, the voice of the Holy Ghost. The mention of the Holy Ghost seemed to decide the specialists that he must be put in an institution. On grounds of his war service, my mother got him admitted to the mental patients' ward of a Canadian veterans' hospital near Montreal. He seemed sunk in melancholia. Once he tried to escape from the hospital, getting as far as the local railroad station; but then, having no money and no clear idea of where he wanted to go, he lost heart and returned to the institution. While he was in this wretched state, my mother got a postcard from him on which he had scrawled the words "nil desperandum". She wept when she read this message.

As the months and the years went by, Gerald's condition changed. His delusions persisted, but his spirits revived, and he became talkative again. My mother visited him regularly, and I went to see him from time to time. Our meetings took place in a sort of tea pavilion adjoining the mental ward. Always hospitable, Gerald would order three or four pots of tea and the same number of plates of buttered toast for the two of us so that the tea table groaned under the load. After a few polite inquiries about one's own activities, he would turn to the subject of the Holy Ghost, with whom he was still in almost constant communication. On one of my visits he told me with the air of one confiding a Cabinet secret that God the Father and the Holy Ghost were much concerned about the behaviour of Jesus Christ.

"They both feel that he is talking too much, making too many speeches. For instance, the Sermon on the Mount, they don't approve of that at all, and they were never consulted. But keep that to yourself."

After tea I said that I must be going as I had to catch the train back to Montreal. Gerald protested: "Don't think of going so soon. It is such a pleasure to see you. You bring a breath of the outside world." Then, leaning back in his chair, he gazed at the ceiling with a far-away expression on his face, and in a plaintive aside (addressed, I suppose, to the Holy Ghost) he uttered: "Oh, how his visit has taken it out of me; Oh, how he tires me!" I hastened to take my departure.

Gerald spent upwards of thirty years in that institution. In the latter part of that time, he ceased hearing voices. His delusions disappeared. My mother suggested that arrangements could be made for him to leave the hospital and live quietly in the country. But he shrank from the idea of facing the outer world again. However, he was well enough to pay short visits to us. He even came to my wedding, clad, as formerly, in a suit much too large for him. I remember a scene in the lobby of the hotel on our way to the wedding reception when my mother, having borrowed some safety pins from the hotel maid, was pinning up Gerald's trousers so that they no longer completely covered his feet.

The last time I saw Gerald was shortly before his death. He was lying propped up in a hospital bed in a ward full of other ailing war veterans. He was over seventy by then, a shrunken, little old man, crippled with arthritis. His twisted hands lay on the blanket before him. He looked both diminished and dignified. Conversation was difficult. I fumbled for subjects which might interest him. Of his fellow patients, he said, a shade patronizingly: "They are good fellows, but they *will* groan, which is so tiresome. There is a very decent clergyman who visits here. They seem to find him a comfort. He means well." He spoke with a kind of dry weariness as though religion was a stimulant of which he had drunk to excess and been cured. I tried the theatre. He still followed news of plays and actors. "Your own songs, Gerald," I ventured in a long pause in the conversation: "You remember?" For a moment a weak flash of his earlier self returned. He tried to straighten up in bed and sang out in a high, thin voice: "I'm Burlington Bertie, I rise at ten thirty," but then shrugged and desisted. As I was leaving the ward, he called me back to his bedside and said in a lowered voice: "A wonderful woman, your mother."

After Gerald's death, I went to the hospital to thank the nurses who had looked after him in his last illness, especially a French-Canadian nurse of whom he was fond, and who had been kind to him. When I spoke of him, she said: "He was so brave, never a word of complaint, and so polite—*si bien élevé.*"

ANNE MARRIOTT

Anne Marriott's story "Mrs. Absalom" was broadcast on Anthology's *third program in November, 1954, and was the first of her many appearances, as a poet and a short-story writer, in the series. She was born in Victoria, B.C., and was active in the founding of Alan Crawley's poetry magazine* Contemporary Verse *in 1941. She was a script editor for the National Film Board in Ottawa in the late 1940s and later moved back to the West Coast; she now lives in North Vancouver. A major collection of her poetry,* The Circular Coast: New and Selected Poems, *was published in 1981, and a collection of her short fiction is to appear in 1984.*

❖

Mrs. Absalom

I was eleven the summer Mrs. Absalom came to the island. July sun lay hot over the west coast, over the sounds and straits, over the Gulf of Georgia where our island was—over all the islands with their dry moss and bare rocks, their pale blotches of cultivated ground and deep dark tracts of forest.

I had been playing ball with the other island youngsters and I was hot. But when we heard the whistle of the little island steamer I got my sweater without being told. However warm the sunny fields, down in the cove there would be a dank chill.

I ran down then to the small wooden jetty, its piles hung with festoons of black, slimy weed. Outside the bay the sea was blue and glittering; inside, the water was dull indigo-green in the shade of the heavy trees.

The steamer turned into the cove, changing from robust white to shadowy grey. She slowed, her propeller churning whirlpools in the dark water. One of the big boys caught the line, hauled in the cable and made it fast. The narrow gangplank thudded on to the wharf. Holding an overstuffed music case awkwardly in her arms, Mrs. Absalom picked her way to shore.

Her face was almost as pale and completely round as one of my mother's steamed English puddings. From it pale, round eyes peered shortsightedly.

The mail was being taken to the store. The other children ran after it up the dusty road, back into the sunshine, to the suspense of letter-sorting, the excitement of ice-cream sent twice weekly from the mainland.

But I had noticed the crew, with several onlookers pressed into service, gathering around the small hold. The woman stepped to the edge of the wharf. She squinted at the hold, she made worried gestures with hands in brownish kid gloves. Curious, I moved closer and saw the immense, rectangular top of something—I could only identify it as *something*—protruding from the vessel's interior. The woman called with sharp nervousness, "Be careful, please!"

The small winch and cables strained and screamed. Slowly the thing inched up from the hold, rose above the small ship, hung swaying and enormous against the background of wild trees across the cove. It was a huge box, taller than it was wide, wider than it was thick, the upper part of the front slanted.

"It's a coffin!" I thought. I jumped back. My stomach rose. Then sense returned. While I had never seen, never wished to see, a coffin, I knew this box was too large, the wrong shape.

It swung, lurched downward, landed with a heavy thud shot through with a peculiar jangling. With perfect timing, as if (I thought years later) curtains opened on a drama about to be played, the front of the box trembled and fell forward with a loud smack on the dock. Inside the box, not a coffin but something else I had never seen, was a piano.

Even to my ignorance, it seemed unusually large. Its ornately carved, highly polished wood glowed in the box with a dark, bossed radiance; the smooth bosom bordered with lustrous grapes and acorns, stylized scrolls and swelling curlicues. It seemed impossible that such wood was related to the splintery boards of the jetty or the live timber in the trees beyond.

A high English voice was raised indignantly to someone but I only heard "Box—carelessness—" I stepped closer to the piano, staring into the unfamiliar shine and gleam, the winking curves, the dark polished sea of the smooth front. For an instant the strange glow of the wood seemed to reach out to me, draw me towards it, suck me in. I pulled back with an effort.

I turned and ran, up the wharf, into the brightness and heat of the dusty road, to the store. I pushed in loudly among the other children, demanding to know if there was mail for us and whether the ice-cream was strawberry or vanilla—or, rapturous occasion, both.

Mrs. Absalom's arrival spurred great comment and wonder among the twenty or so households dotting the island. She had bought the old Fawcett place, a rambling dwelling with an acre or so of badly cleared land, overgrown fruit trees, an uncertain well. But why had she come? Curious visitors were politely repelled.

"Typical English," said the storekeeper who had come from the States years back. "Keeps herself to herself, as they say. Wouldn't open up at all when I was serving her."

My mother fared differently. Perhaps because of her welling of natural sympathy, perhaps because she too was English, having been brought from the Midland Counties to British Columbia in her teens. In any case, after an extended call on Mrs. Absalom, she told us indignant details.

"Imagine, that poor thing, buying the old Fawcett place without seeing it! But the real estate agent"—my mother kept her most biting tones for real estate agents—"assured her it was a charming cottage, ideal for a woman alone."

Mrs. Absalom had come also from a Midland town, my mother told us, and had been a professional pianist. But she had had a breakdown. The doctors advised complete change of scene. She came to British Columbia and there had met—oh, unfortunate day —Mr. Absalom, a charming middle-aged gentleman of vague origin with, it appeared later, no money and almost no compunction. Eventually, in the company of a younger, prettier, and wealthier English arrival Mr. Absalom met his death in a car accident. Mrs. Absalom, her capital almost gone, attempted to extend a pittance sent (with her clothes) by better-off English relatives by teaching music. She was not a success.

In panic, she decided to put what money she had left into a country cottage where she could at least enjoy her music. She loved the gardens of England and Victoria. She would have a garden. With what she grew and the tiny allowance, she could stay alive.

As Mother rose to clear the table she announced to me, "You can have music lessons. I've always wanted you to. And it will be a way of helping her—tactfully."

The memory of the piano, glowing in its box, rushed on me. I was afraid. Then fear dissolved in fascination. "Okay," I conceded.

"Don't say 'okay'," Mother reproved, "you're not an American."

I had always been clumsy-fingered and nervousness made it worse. That winter was a torment. As we had no piano I had to walk to the old Fawcett place daily to practise under Mrs. Absalom's supervision. She would pace the sagging floor with short, quick steps, her round face tensed in an agonized network of lines which seemed added to daily as I stumbled up arpeggios and down scales. Finally she would rush to the piano, "No, no, stop it, stop it! Start again—like *this*—"

I could not have learned music in any case on that piano. As I practised, I stole glances into the swelling shine of the bosom in front of me, glimpsing my own unhappy face, darkly reflected, Mrs. Absalom's despairing movements behind me and, behind her, the window framing the tangle of huge old fruit trees and wild evergreens beyond.

But only for a moment could I look. Any longer, and I would feel myself leaning towards that shining pool of wood, looking into brown depths that in one more instant would draw me toppling off the stool down into—I never knew. I pulled my eyes away while my fingers scrabbled on wrong notes and Mrs. Absalom groaned.

I had discovered cherubs among the carvings, with tiny wooden eyes. I felt them watch me as I played. The glints on acorn and grape and berry became eyes too, all intent on me. I would try to hurry, to escape, dreadful dissonance under my hands until Mrs. Absalom stopped me and I had to start all over again.

The climax came the day I swore. I had tried a score of times on one black-noted scale. Finally, "Oh, hell," I said, throwing my arms with a climactic jangle on the keys, my head on my arms. I began to sob.

For a minute Mrs. Absalom talked, outraged and icy, about the language of a lady. Then she stopped. We looked at each other, human being to human being. "It's no good, is it?" she said quietly. "It's no good," I agreed.

"Tell your mother I'm very sorry," she said. She handed me my music and we shook hands like two adults.

After that, oddly, Mrs. Absalom and I became friends. As spring came on, I went over several afternoons a week to help her with her garden. She had got very thin as winter ended. "Starving herself," my mother averred. But politely, Mrs. Absalom rejected Mother's offered pork pies and sausage rolls, with pride Mother regretted but understood.

Now the long-untended soil of the old Fawcett place was frantically planted with multiple rows of peas, carrots, beetroot, herbs. Mrs. Absalom hacked out holes for small nut trees to substitute for the meat she could seldom afford. She wrested pieces off the old fruit trees—trees which seemed to have caught the fierce growth of the forest beyond and spread and soared, almost indecently prolific of leaf and bloom.

One June day a soft Pacific sky softened further into rain, enough to drive us indoors. "Please play to me," I asked on impulse.

"I must wash my hands," she said, holding them out in an absent gesture. They were soiled deeply, for she became impatient with gloves as she handled delicate seedlings. She noticed my stare, looked at her hands herself. A startled look came on her oddly round small face.

She went into the kitchen, pumped water, rubbed soap violently into her palms, scrubbed at each finger with a brush. Still with the bewildered look on her pudding face, she sat slowly down at the piano. For the first time I heard her strike several wrong notes.

I drifted over to stand behind her. The polish of the piano bosom had lost the high lustre of the winter. Cautiously, I peered into it over Mrs. Absalom's shoulder. I could not see my own face but focussed a reflection of hers.

Suddenly, by some trick of light or movement of my own, an image of the trees outside, pears and pines, towered into the wooden mirror. They seemed to sweep forward, engulfing the pale globule of Mrs. Absalom's face with a violence that made me jump back.

She did not notice. She struck another wrong note and abruptly closed the piano. "The garden is coming along nicely now. I shall soon be able to practise properly," she said.

I was edging away. "I'd better go." It was still raining, but this made an excuse for running until the image of the trees in the piano front began to fade.

After that day, except on one occasion, much later, I never looked into the wooden bosom again.

That fall, I was sent to a small boarding-school in Vancouver. I had measles all my Christmas holidays, and when summer came we all made a long-discussed trip to Mother's home in England. In the welter of new excitements, I did not get to see Mrs. Absalom for nearly two years.

When I saw her, I thought she had shrunk—dried up like the fruit which was packed on the window sills, on racks in the kitchen. Her face was like a dried apple, pale, drawn into a multitude of tight creases.

After a while I asked her to play to me. The huge piano had been pushed tightly against the wall, islanded in a sea of small nuts drying to some formula recalled from a childhood gardener. I saw that the carved berries and acorns no longer twinkled, as if dying like the once-living fruits around the room. The cherubs were blind with dust.

Mrs. Absalom sat down on the bench. She lifted her hands. We both looked at them, as we had once before. They were dark brown now, soil-ingrained, rough to horniness. "Come at Christmas, come at Christmas!" she cried with a peculiar shrillness. "I'll have had time to practise by Christmas!"

But we spent Christmas in Vancouver that year. Next summer, I went with a school friend to her Cariboo ranch, coming home for only a week before fall term started. When I said casually that I was going to see Mrs. Absalom, Mother demurred.

"You've got plenty to do here, dear—" Then, when I stared, "Sometimes—when people have had all the trouble Mrs. Absalom has had, they become—not queer exactly—" As I pressed for an explanation, "Well, it was the piano most of all—"

I had not consciously thought of the piano for months but now my mind whirled with grapes and curlicues, scrolls and cherubs. I thought of the vast polished bosom, so dulled when I last saw it.

"She moved it out into the front garden," Mother said.

It was the most horrifying thing I had ever imagined, much less heard of. A nausea I thought long outgrown shook my stomach. "She didn't, she couldn't!"

Mother misunderstood. "I wouldn't have believed she could—it seemed impossible. But somehow she did it, a little at a time. Her muscles are really strong from gardening, I suppose. Though I'm afraid she must have strained—it was really because of the trees that she moved it. It's extraordinary how they've grown, even for the coast. The nut trees in particular. Her whole house was full of nuts drying, but she still didn't have enough room so she moved the piano out."

My father, who had been sitting in silence as usual, suddenly took up the story. He made the tale more horrifying by his unheard-of loquacity.

"I wanted to buy the piano," he said. "Don't care for music but I do know a good piece of wood when I see it. But she wouldn't think of it. She could practise out-of-doors, she said. More than that—" He glanced at Mother, who shook her head, but he ignored her.

"Last time I went over to suggest buying it she was working among the nut trees—had a pair of pruning-shears in her hand. Always pruning, but can never keep up with all the growth. When I said, 'About the piano—' she glared at me through those round glasses and then she took a tight grip on the shears and rushed right at me, the shears out ahead of her.

" 'If you dare talk of taking my piano away again, I'll—kill you,' she said. When she got to 'kill' she seemed to hear what she was saying. She looked sort of bewildered, as if she'd heard something that frightened her and didn't know where it came from. She said, 'Excuse me, I have work to do, so much work—' and went back into the filberts."

"He went over next day"—Mother didn't like being silent for so long—"when Mrs. Absalom had gone to the store, and covered the piano all around with tarpaulins—covered it well, didn't you?"

"Yes," my father said, sighing. "But the damp will come up from the ground. It'll come up and ruin it. And it was such fine wood."

It was that autumn that my father began the long illness which led to my parents' selling their place on the island and moving to Vancouver. We quickly lost touch with the old life.

I was twenty that bright, fall holiday morning when I decided on the spur of the moment to take the little coastal steamer, which still meandered among the islands, and stop over the four hours at our old home.

With a handful of summer trippers, I went up the road from the new wharf to the freshly painted store. There was a new young storekeeper. Buying an ice-cream cone (they had tutti-frutti now) I asked him, in an urge to find familiarity somewhere, "How's Mrs. Absalom?"

"Mrs—? Oh, that batty old English dame. Don't know—haven't seen her for weeks."

Before you came to the old Fawcett place there was an open space of grass and rocks. I remembered one could see the house from here, but now even the chimneys were hidden in a mountain of foliage and heavy branches. The firs with their sharp tips were above them all, then, as I came nearer, I picked out the old rambling overgrown apples, the pear trees poking knottily into the sky. Lower again, and thickest of all, were the nut trees.

The cement path to the front door was broken and tossed about. I was stepping carefully but nearly stumbled when I became aware of an enormous, mould-coloured bulk beside me. It gave me only a little reassurance to realize it was the piano, still covered with my father's now-rotting tarpaulin.

The tarp was stained with weather and bird-droppings. Hidden underneath would be the broad bosom of the piano, the cherubs and acorns in God-knew-what state. I lifted my hand to try to pull the cover aside and see the wood and carving but the fabric ripped in my hand and I left it alone. I turned to the door. It stood open.

Dust lay deep on the furniture in the room where I had so often struggled with Czerny and arpeggios. The floor was covered with dusty sheets of paper on which innumerable early windfall apples had been heaped. They were piled on boxes, tables, and a rough trestle bench. Many of the apples were bruised and browning; a smell heavy with sadness and decay was in the room.

"Mrs. Absalom!" I called. I knocked loudly on the doorpost. "Mrs. Absalom!"

There was no answer. I went hesitantly into the house. Everywhere was dust, everywhere was fruit, was vegetables, put ready for canning or heaped to ripen or dry. None of it was fresh, firm or shapely; the odour of fermentation and rot increased. "Mrs. Absalom!" The kitchen was empty, the stained stove cold.

I plunged down the back steps into the vast tangle of garden, a wilderness of leaf and stem; huge juicy weeds, carrots run to tops like ornamental shrubs. Even the wasps feeding on the broken pears under the giant, rheumatic trees looked larger than normal.

"Mrs. Absalom!"

I remembered my father had made her what he called a garden seat, a bench with back where she would take a brief rest with an outdated English magazine, in her early days at the Fawcett place. The seat was on a patch of weedy lawn, hedged rather prettily then with the young nut trees.

I pushed my way through the thick foliage of the filberts, under the snakelike boughs of the walnuts, into what was now a dank cave under the branches. The seat was still there, but tumbled onto its back. For no reason its awkward, upset position gave me a feeling of panic.

"Mrs. Absalom!" I almost screamed it.

I stared around the hollow space, then upward into the thick nut trees and saw what would, however long I lived, be the most terrible sight of my life.

It was a pair of feet, bunioned, spread feet in greyish-brown stockings, in brownish-grey canvas shoes. They were hanging, with extraordinary limpness and pointlessness, among the branches of the largest walnut.

It appeared that Mrs. Absalom had not, as I thought when I saw the overturned seat, hanged herself, nor had she been caught by the head in the branches like her Biblical namesake. She had had an ordinary stroke, while struggling up the tree, and, falling, had been caught between boughs and held there. I did not ask if she had died immediately.

It also appeared that my father and mother were executors of Mrs. Absalom's estate—so-called. My father, now well again if looking old, left immediately for the island.

I got there, on special leave from my stenography job, just before the funeral service was due to begin in the tiny Anglican church. The coffin was already outside the building on a rough trolley.

Mother was waiting for me. "Look at the lid of the coffin," she said in an undertone.

I stepped over to the trolley, reluctantly. I looked down—and drifted forward into a polished, deep brown pool, while cherubs with sharp wooden eyes, winking grapes and scrolls, oak leaves with eyes in every lobe, regarded me from around the rim.

I leaned over and my face swam into focus, clouds and treetops moving behind it. There were vague shapes farther in the wooden pool and they seemed to form into the huge oblong of a box, the pale circle of a face, the palmate shapes of hands darkened with soil.

I leaned farther, trying to summon that old feeling of sinking down, of being drawn in irresistibly, wanting to plumb the bottom of the brown pool and find out what had lurked or I had dreamed there, what had fascinated and frightened me, before it was too late.

"Wonderful wood," said my father in a whisper. I straightened up. "I knew how to treat it," he went on. "Fitted the pieces of the border around the edge of the casket. Thought the poor soul should have something nice to be buried in, at least. Rest of the piano was past saving, I gather."

I slipped into the church as four men began to move the coffin towards the shallow steps. The candles on the altar made a faint illumination in the noon-day darkness cast by the tall trees outside the pointed, greenish glass windows.

PHYLLIS WEBB

Although Phyllis Webb has had several careers, her true vocation has always been that of poet. She is a graduate of the University of British Columbia and has taught there and at the University of Alberta and the University of Victoria. In the late 1960s she was executive producer of the CBC radio series Ideas. *She has broadcast talks, reviews and poetry readings on many CBC programs. Phyllis Webb now lives and writes on Saltspring Island near Vancouver. The four "Portraits" published here appear in a collection of her poetry,* Wilson's Bowl *(Coach House, 1980), and were read by Phyllis Webb herself on* Anthology.

❖

Kropotkin

Consider the dead
for whom we make elegies
how they differently
instruct us.
I have been studying
K. on his deathbed
a pine frond arranged
into the photographer's
lustrous design
and lace and a white
pillow for bedding death
for a still life
incidental to the grand
pianos hammering out
in Moscow and Petrograd
love domiciled in lace
pine & pillow in Dmitrov
in Dmitrov a son of man
domesticated, a wild idea
whose face is noble

and kindly, a prince
of a man waxing into
a death's head
a great dome, home
his *Ethics* unfinished...
the reaches of his mind
so vast and intimate...
O Socrate! (*"la langue
paralysée et suis
incapable...."*)
his white beard
where the morning stars
sang...

For Fyodor

I am a beetle in the cabbage soup they serve up for geniuses
in the House of the Dead.

I am a black beetle and loll seductively at the bottom of the
warm slop.

Someday, Fyodor, by mistake you'll swallow me down and I'll
  become
a part of your valuable gutworks.

In the next incarnation I hope to imitate that idiot and saint,
Prince Myshkin, drop off my wings for his moronic glory.

Or, if I miss out on the Prince, Sonya or Dunya might do.

I'm not joking. I am not the result of bad sanitation in the
kitchen, as you think.

Up here in Omsk in Siberia beetles are not accidents but destinies.

I'm drowning fast, but even in this condition I realize your bad
tempered haughtiness is part of your strategy.

You are about to turn this freezing hell into an ecstatic emblem.
A ferocious shrine.

Ah, what delicious revenge. But take care! A fit is coming!
Now, now I'll leap into your foaming mouth and jump your
     tongue.
Now I stamp on this not quite famous tongue

shouting: Remember Fyodor, you may hate men but it's here in
Omsk you came to love mankind.

But you don't hear, do you: there you are writhing in epileptic
visions.

Hold your tongue! You can't speak yet. You are mine, Dostoevsky.

I aim to slip down your gullet and improve myself.
I can almost hear what you'll say:

> Crime and Punishment
> Suffering and Grace

and of the dying

> pass by and forgive
> us our happiness

Ezra Pound

And among the divine paranoids old Ezra
paces his cage unattached to the mode of doubt

replete with salvation he is 60 years old
under the Pisan sunfire. He sees straight
through the bars into the court of Confucius
then slumps in a corner wondering what went
wrong. His old man's hair is matted with rain
and wardust. His brain is in fever.
Nevertheless he hikes from pole to pole
to plot once more the stars of his fixed
obsession. It seems so clear. If only
they'd listened. They shine light all night
on the perplexity of his predicament.
He stares back, can't sleep, understands
nothing. Jew-hater. Poet. Intellectual.
A curious animal, a-typical, it reads and
writes, shaking and sweating, being so shut in,
the canto arising:

> *"And if the corn cat be beaten*
> *Demeter has lain in my furrow"*

the mode of doubt imprisoned for ever and ever
in the style of its own luxury.

Rilke

Rilke, I speak your name I throw it away
with your angels, your angels, your statues
and virgins, and a horse in a field held
at the hoof by wood. I cannot take so much
tenderness, tenderness, snow falling like lace
over your eyes year after year as the poems
receded, roses, the roses, sinking in snow
in the distant mountains.

Go away with your women to Russia or take them
to France, and take them or don't the poet is
in you, the spirit, they love that.
(I met one in Paris, her death leaning outward,
death in all forms. The letters you'd sent her,
she said, stolen from a taxi.)

Rilke.
Clowns and angels held your compassion.
You could sit in a room saying nothing,
nothing. Your admirers thought you were there,
a presence, a wisdom. But you had to leave
everyone once, once at least. That was your
hardness.

This page is a shadowed hall in Duino Castle.
Echoes. The echoes.
I don't know why I'm here.

MARIAN ENGEL

Marian Engel has been a vigorous presence on the literary scene both as a writer of novels, short stories and books for children and as an activist in the Writers' Union and other groups and organizations working to improve the situation of Canadian writers. She was educated at McMaster and McGill universities and studied French literature in Provence. She lives in Toronto.

One of Marian Engel's novels, Joanne, *was written as a serial reading for CBC radio, and* The Glassy Sea, *which many critics regard as her best novel, was read on the CBC series* Book Time *in the winter of 1984. Many of her short stories have been heard on* Anthology, *including "Amaryllis", which has been published in her one collection of short fiction,* Inside the Easter Egg *(House of Anansi, 1975).*

❦

Amaryllis

He was the cleanest baby they had ever seen, so fastidious that his mother was worried about him. His nanny, however, assured her that he was a bright little fellow; and wasn't it a blessing to have a sweet little boy after all the big lolloping girls.

He was not sure why he was obsessed with order: it had something to do, he thought, with the hugeness of everyone around him, which amounted (because he remained undersize until he had chicken pox in his late teens and "shot up") to gross indecency since he viewed his parents and his sisters from low and unflattering angles. What he was sure of was that for him, everything had to be tidy and intact. He knew it annoyed his family, he knew that his mother particularly considered him to be lacking in spirit, and also, from a very early age, that he was, himself, complete as an egg, and would always be this way, and annoy them.

They were prosperous; they lived in one of the great solid houses on the mountain of Montreal; there was never any problem with money. When he decided to make his career in the university, where he could order facts as he ordered his life, no one protested. This was not the kind of mind that would bring scope and drive to the family business, it was a fussy mind, it might, even, for all they knew, be the mind of a homosexual. They gave him his choice of the universities. He went to McGill and Harvard and Oxford and was very happy, and obstinately although fastidiously heterosexual.

His trouble with women was, however, that he liked intellectual women, and the intellectual women he ran into were not interested in housekeeping, and he had friends with similar problems. None of them wanted to marry cows who ran splendid establishments but had nothing to say, but the good minds they met refused to deal with cupboards and scrubbing brushes or even servants. Gloomily, and perhaps too earnestly, he tested his women friends and came to the conclusion that the man who said that brainy women don't wash their hair was right.

Thus he was a bachelor of thirty-one, and well established in his field, when he accepted a vacancy in his discipline at McGill and returned to Montreal, not, firmly, to the house on the mountain, but to a modern bachelor apartment which he fitted with books and white blankets, glass and white plastic furniture, white broadloom.

His mother, having fallen into the habit of introducing young people to each other when she was marrying off the girls (she had done this with distinction), immediately arranged a set of dinner parties for him. His work load was heavy, and he would dash home looking (for him) dishevelled, and sit grumpily in the grand dining-room beside or across from the candidates she had chosen, who were on the whole ill-formed or ill-informed, for the girls of their set who had wits had gambolled away on their own years ago. Some of them, he knew, were both brainy and neat and he had missed his chance with them.

So for most of his first year at McGill he was unhappy, and he earned the reputation of being not an eligible bachelor, but a crusty one, though his social coinage remained valuable because of his surname. Towards the end of his second term, at an inter-departmental meeting, he ran into a friend of his undergraduate days, a gusty left-wing anthropologist called Ziggy Taler, an irrepressibly untidy man, but a brilliant one. He took Ziggy, who was between wives, home for a drink after the meeting.

"Christ, Alex," Ziggy said, looking around the bachelor nest, "you're the same as ever. Everything in rows and all white. Is it a complex?"

"I don't think so. I think I was born this way."

"Ruthie used to say I was an ink-blot sprouting cigar ash. Couldn't stand me." It was an accurate comparison: he sprawled in the armchair with his tie askew and often missed the ashtray.

This was not, however, the kind of disorder that pained Alexander. Things broken and out of their places upset him, and leaky taps and stockings dripping: ash could be vacuumed.

"I hear," said Ziggy, "that the gold-rush is coming to an end. Both your mother and Mrs. Challenor have given up the struggle to find you a wife."

"I hope so."

"Working on a new book?"

"I'm doing the index."

"Yourself? Christ, man, what you need is a round little blonde graduate student. Let me know when you want to come up for air and I'll take you around to meet some people. It's time you got out of that goddam Harvard-Oxford-Westmount ghetto."

Ziggy disappeared for the summer, and Alexander flew to London to check references at the British Museum and attend conferences, but in the fall, finding himself at last with free time, he started dropping in at Ziggy's apartment, where he was liable to meet women of all colours, habits and descriptions, most of whom considered him a reactionary because of his family connections (which were not disguised by his surname) and discussed him unflatteringly to his face. One night, among them, he found a gaunt American poetess named Amaryllis.

She was as tall as his sisters, but differently made, a walking skeleton with large joints and a lantern jaw. She had the hollow voice of the buck-teethed, and tight, straggly blonde curls, and a great mat of blonde hair on her arms and legs. Ziggy told him she was mad as a hatter; that she had finished at the university but had not been able either to face graduate work or to find a job. "She's bright enough," he said, "but undirected. God, can you imagine anyone focussing that and sending it all off in the same direction?"

She talked fast, but the hollow voice seemed to run behind the mouthing and the gestures, to come from a speaker somewhere else. She seemed by turns naive and supremely wise; she had great, haunted china-blue eyes.

The next day he went with some trepidation to buy her book of poems at Heinemann's. As he was picking it out, the bookseller said, "You'll find that the girl is very good, I assure you." This frightened him. He saved the book until after dinner. (He cooked for himself, and with finesse.) He found that Heinemann was right, and fell in love with Amaryllis.

She was the child of American eccentrics of good family who had chosen, after *Walden*, to live in the country, and off the land. She had had a queer, isolated childhood, backwoods Maine alternating with expensive boarding-schools, and still seemed unsure what to do in a city. When he took her to restaurants she spilled her soup or her wine. She got very drunk, very fast. He found himself adoring her words, and entertaining her more and more in his apartment. He then prudently rented a larger one (she was all right if the pieces of furniture were far enough apart, otherwise she knocked over his little Knoll tables and bumped into bric-à-brac). When he found that she wasn't actually living anywhere, only with this friend or that, he asked her to live with him, and, at the end of the year, they decided to marry.

His mother, surprisingly, took to her, though she was annoyed when the engagement received large notice in the *New York Times*, for in addition to the sin of being an American, Amaryllis had committed the solecism of being a pedigreed American (the notice was sent to the papers out of some dim memory of her mother's about how things had once been done) with a list of ancestors beside which Alexander's family looked *nouveau riche*, and was.

They were married in the Cathedral between Eaton's and Morgan's, Amaryllis wearing her great-grandmother's yellowish lace and satin, which was not too small. Alexander's sisters attended her and Ziggy was best man: there was a six-inch discrepancy in height between the men's and the women's sides at the altar.

For the first year of their marriage, they went about in a trance. They were both lonely people, and now they were committed to keep each other company. They liked many of the same things, although Amaryllis did not entertain—indeed, she neither knew nor cared about entertaining—she was superbly active, she took him out of himself into sections of the city he had never before penetrated. She fitted into every milieu and did surprisingly well with the academics, and exercised her lively mind on films and plays. Her French was good—indeed, she seemed to lose a good deal of her awkwardness when she translated herself into the more feminine language—and she took him to parties where by himself he would simply have been another Westmount bastard. When they were home alone, he did the cooking. He kept his cleaning woman, and thought that Amaryllis did not notice when he remade their bed, to smooth the creases in the sheets, which hurt him.

About the time when he was beginning his first draft of the third book, however, she became pregnant. She was very sick, and after that, very sleepy. She spent all day in bed surrounded by Kleenex and newspapers and basins and trays and could not be shunted into the winter cold. His mother and his nanny came to visit her, and, nodding wisely to each other, began to buy for the baby. Amaryllis read Dr. Spock in bed and asked him to make love whenever he passed the bedroom door. She phoned a department store and ordered nursery furniture, then discovered belatedly that they would need a bedroom for it. They moved.

The baby was born in the spring. She called him Tod. Alexander, irritably hoping to be able to spend the summer on his book, noticed that though she spent all her time with him, she rarely changed him. He was, furthermore, although a well-dispositioned baby, inclined towards projectile vomiting. The house, which neither of them took much interest in, began to smell.

When he suggested that his elderly nanny come to help, she was angry, and he discovered that she held firm and clear ideas on the subject of child-raising. Tod was not, she insisted, to be turned into a fussy child. Everything was to be nerveless and casual, the child was not to be sacrificed to the furniture or the upholstery; if there were sacred objects he should move them to his study upstairs.

Amaryllis-mother was not the same person as Amaryllis-poet. He consoled himself that most men make the same discovery about their wives, he was involved in an extreme situation because he had married an extreme woman. His work load, however, increased the next year, and it was disheartening to come home to no supper. She learned to scramble a decent egg for Tod, and often made the same effort for him, but the sight of Amaryllis with a paring-knife was unbearable, for she was as uncoordinated as ever, she could barely change Tod without swallowing his pins, so that he went on having to do the cooking, and since the cleaning woman had left, the vacuuming (Amaryllis and the machine together suffered from a plethora of elbows), and he phoned the baby-sitters as well because she hated to leave Tod, and by the end of the year he was fed to the teeth with marriage.

Tod was a beautiful child, with his mother's fair curls and his father's neat limbs; but he was also a child: he cut up a paper Alex was preparing for the Learned Societies, he rose early and poured ink on the white rugs. Amaryllis began to look guiltily at Alex. Alex began to glower.

"Why don't you write poetry any more?" he asked.

She did not know, she said. It had something to do with freedom. You wrote poetry, if you wanted to write good poetry, when your mind was free, and she did not feel free any more. But she warned him not to take it out on Tod.

They went north with a tent that summer. It rained all the time. Amaryllis began to have fits of crying.

When they returned to Montreal, she went on crying—everything seemed to be beyond her. "You should try not to," he said, "it frightens the child."

"The child, is that all he is to you?"

"Tod, then."

"You never make love to me any more."

"You're always asleep or accursed."

She began to cry again.

"You ought to see a psychiatrist."

Then she exploded. "Is that what you think, Alex? Do you think I'm crazy because I'm unhappy with you? Is that your solution? Neither Toddy nor I have been able to put a foot right for a year. Whenever you look at us a martyred smile crosses your face. We're your cross to bear. You don't even speak to us, you just go around tidying up after us. Why don't you admit you can't stand us?"

He could make no such admission. He did love them, but in such an environment—in the mess, in the stifling hurly-burly of their childishness—he could express nothing.

A week later she took Tod to visit friends in Toronto. She never came back. Alex sold the house and moved his tattered goods to an apartment.

He made vagrant efforts to stay in touch with them, sent them money, sent friends to see that Toddy was well taken care of, sent her new books he thought she would like. Legally, he supposed, he might have assured the return of the child to him, but he could not part them. He went on with his work, feeling empty and failed, and taught in a small mumbling voice, and was neater and neater.

Amaryllis wrote him several long letters saying she still loved him, explaining the basic disjuncture of their souls, saying Toddy missed him. After a while he heard that she had gone to live with another poet in the country. When she asked for a divorce, he made it easy for her, and, as she had asked, put away money for Tod's education.

Ziggy Taler was disgusted with him. "You let a good girl go without even putting up a fight."

"I suppose I don't like fighting."

"I know, it's not neat. You're turning into an old woman."

"Perhaps I always was one."

When the Separatist movement began to make itself seriously felt, he left Montreal. He belonged by birth to the other camp but Amaryllis and her friends had destroyed his loyalty to it. He did not feel that there was a place for him in the city except as an example of the dying vitality of the WASP strain.

He went south, across the border, and taught at a mid-Western university. The change invigorated him. He began to get his confidence back. His new book on international relations made him a minor celebrity.

When he was offered a job at Toronto, Toddy was eight years old. Alex found that Amaryllis was still living in the country, and had put out two books that he had not seen. He accepted the position.

Soon after he settled in Toronto, he met a girl very like himself, admirably suited to him: clever, neat, quiet, serious. She knew Amaryllis; she had in fact edited her poems. She agreed to marry him, but did not wish to have children, for her career was well established, but not adaptable to long interruptions. She thought, however, that it might be good for Tod to come and visit them in the school holiday.

Except for a blank meeting over the divorce, when they had not been themselves but dry papier-mâché lawyers' puppets, he had not seen Amaryllis for over six years. He drove north to visit her now, following a map she had sent with a cordial invitation.

They were living on the stony scrublands south of Algonquin Park, along a dirt road that seemed miles from anywhere. Her map was inaccurate, but the village post office knew them well, and directed him. It was afternoon when he drove up their corduroy lane.

Tod, a thin, brown lad with his own face, stopped him half-way. "She's chopping wood, mister," he said. "We don't interrupt her." Axe-blows fell far apart in the distance, ringing in the clear country air. "Are you Alex?" the child asked. He nodded, and Tod took his hand.

They walked up to the house—a cottage with unpainted board-and-batten siding—when the sound of the axe had stopped. Amaryllis came out beaming, carrying a baby.

He saw her with an awful surge of devotion. Living so much

outdoors had consolidated her, she was brown and fat, her faded print blouse was pushed out at the buttons. "Well, Alex, this is Sabina." The baby was fat, too, and ruddy, far different from the waxy infant Tod. He smiled weakly at her.

"Bill's in the woodlot—Tod, run and get him. We're getting the wood in for the winter."

He looked around him and for the first time noticed the blazing autumn colour.

"Come in, I'll make you some tea."

The main room of the house contained a woodstove, a crib, and a big pine table surrounded by ladder-back chairs. One end held a collection of instant-coffee bottles. "I'm putting up jam," she said. Then, "I like it here. It's the way I was brought up, you know. I'm sorry I couldn't manage in the city."

"I'm sorry I couldn't either."

"I hear you're marrying Sue. She's exactly right for you."

He was too unhappy to answer.

"We make wine, too. Here, this is Bill's elderberry."

It tasted like cough medicine, but it cheered him, or at least cleared his throat so that he could speak again. But as he opened his mouth there was a commotion in the lane.

"Oh Lord, it's the CBC, they're filming us today. Who'll I say you are? Do you know anyone there? Can I say you're from my publishers?" She handed him Sabina, who began to cry, and then barfed on his shoulder.

Tod and Bill—a bear of a man with a black beard got up to look like a voyageur—came pelting out of the bush. Tod took the baby from him, Bill pumped his hand. "I hear you want young Tod for the holidays."

"If he wants to come."

Amaryllis called out, "Alex, is the cabin tidy?" and dashed in through the screen door. "Oh hell, it looks like us, anyway. They can come in." Alex made his excuses.

"It's the worst possible day," she said. "Come again, will you?"

He made his way back to his car past men with cords and video cameras.

Tod came at Easter, since they had agreed by letter that the roads would be too difficult at Christmas, and quietly submitted to expeditions to the Museum and the theatre. But at night he sobbed in his sleep and called out for Amaryllis and Sabina.

On the fourth day Alex asked him if he would like to go home. He said, "Yes please," avoiding his father's eye. He packed his own suitcase in the neatest possible manner.

Alex left him at the bottom of some frozen lane and thought that he wouldn't see him again until he was embarking for some foreign war.

PHYLLIS GOTLIEB

Phyllis Gotlieb wrote "Doctor Umlaut's Earthly Kingdom" on a commission from the CBC for broadcast on Anthology *in 1970. It is one of four verse dramas, all written for CBC radio, that have been published in* The Works: Collected Poems of Phyllis Gotlieb *(Calliope Press, 1978). Since its first broadcast, "Doctor Umlaut" has also been staged successfully by high school and university drama groups in several Ontario cities.*

Phyllis Gotlieb was born in Toronto and still lives there. Beginning with the novel Sunburst *in 1964, she has become a science-fiction writer with an international reputation. Her other science-fiction novels are* O Master Caliban!, A Judgment of Dragons, *and* Emperor, Swords, Pentacles. *A collection of her science-fiction short stories,* Son of the Morning and Other Stories, *was published in 1983.*

❀

Doctor Umlaut's Earthly Kingdom

BARITONE:
   Good evening

SOPRANO:
   good evening

TENOR:
   good evening

ALTO:
   hullo

ALL:
> if you want to know who we are we're a
> bunch of worn-out carnies putting up a crummy
> carnival in a vacant lot

UNDERTAKER *(tenor)*:
> I'm a former seller of potato-peelers and
> ex-vendor of eggbeaters
> who fell into the undertaking business
> because that's where the money is

GIRL *(soprano)*:
> I'm an innocent country lass
> who was betrayed

WHORE *(alto)*:
> I'm a whore with a heart of brass

CLOCKSELLER *(tenor)*:
> I'm-a-highly-nervous-and-unstable-seller-of
> clocks-and-watches-and-I-don't-think-I'll-be
> able-to-stop-talking-till-I-die

MISSUS BROWN *(soprano, a bit over-ripe and sly)*:
> I'm Missus Brown, dear

ALTO:
> what are we waiting for?

TENOR:
> the man coming
> down the street

SOPRANO:
> down the twilight street

TENOR:
> the magisterial man
> with the top hat frock coat snakehead cane
> and everything that goes with that

ALTO:
spade beard striped pants grey spats
and he's carrying
a black case

ALL:
good evening

UMLAUT *(baritone)*:
good evening

Ladies and gentlemen I address you here at the busy
crossroads of life
I watch your cheerful faces and
listen to your happy laughter as you pass in the
street
and I know what misery pain sorrow heartache
and grief those smiles cover that laughter drowns those
cheerful voices conceal
and
to ease those aches those pains those griefs
I am bringing you

release!

for I am Doctor Umlaut! Doctor Umlaut!
and I bring you Doctor Umlaut's
King of Pain!

Doctor Umlaut's Panacea
Panchreston and Pharmacopeia!

wherever it gets you you rub it on
one touch of heaven and the pain is gone

ONLOOKER *(tenor)*:
but I ain't feelin no pain

UMLAUT:
then wait for the rain!
everybody hurts in this vale of sorrow
if you don't get it today it'll get you tomorrow

in this pure glass bottle
no cheap plastic
price one dollar
plus five cents tax
and I'll tell you what it does:

ONLOOKER 2 *(alto)*:
    Doctor, will it cure my sacroiliac?

UMLAUT:
    rub it in!
    if not you get your money back
    if you hurry to catch me, I'm a busy man
    and I've got to make a dollar wherever I can

ONLOOKER 3 *(soprano)*:
    will it cure a sliver?

UMLAUT:
    rub it in!
    crisis, phthisis, fever, liver
    catalepsy, narcolepsy, lycanthropy
    ringworm, tapeworm, hookworm, bookworm
    follicle mites
    everything that bites!

ONLOOKER 1:
    will it cure my hog?

UMLAUT:
    rub it in!
    it'll cure your hog and your sheep and your dog
    springhalt, windgalls, cracked teats
    ringbone, garget, spavins and grease
    sweeney, fistula, foundered feet
    rub it in! rub it in! rub it in!

    if you're stained with sin
    rub it in!
    if you're plagued with doubt
    wipe it out!

if your heart is broken
glue it together
paint it on the sky and change the weather

DISTURBERS *(tenor, alto):*
yeah, yeah, blah, blah!
ah rub it out, Umlaut
Umlaut!

DISTURBERS *(tenor, alto, soprano):*
if you're thirty-six years old and still wet the bed
can't make it with the girls, got a hole in your head
want your grandma brought back from the dead
ask Umlaut, Umlaut—out! out!
(not quite in unison)
go back where you came from, Umlaut
we don't want you here
Umlauts belong with circumflexes

DISTURBER 1 *(alto):*
nah, they're kin to the asterixes

DISTURBER 2 *(tenor):*
commas

DISTURBER 3 *(soprano):*
codicils

DISTURBER 1:
you mean colophons, moron!

ALL THREE:
ah, go back home to the ampersands
Umlaut!

UMLAUT:
Umlaut, I'm Umlaut
lout, I'm Umlaut!

fools, don't laugh
don't sneer

heed the words of the prophet and seer!
for he has decreed
and he has declared

that the laughter of fools
is as the crackling of thorns
beneath the cauldrons of hell
wherein the demons dwell

when the doors are darkened
and the evening cools
when the sound of the grinders
whispers down the street

they're whetting their pitchforks
and sharpening their horns
for the laughter of thorns
is as the crackling of fools!

but if you're so sure that you're absolutely pure
as the snow that falls before the morning light
then go away
who wants you to stay?
an ounce of prevention's worth a pound of cure

and I'll tell *you*
what you can do:

if you don't want to sin eat Christie's crackers
they're sealed in
if you don't want to crack use Polyfilla
it caulks back
if you don't want to fall nail your skin to the wall
if you don't want to crawl give Avis a call
if you don't want to crack
if you don't want to fall
if you don't want to sin

but if you belong to the human race
got eyes ears nose and a mouth in your face
if you turn and turn and never find a place
freeze in the sun and burn in the rain

then you need Doctor Umlaut's King of Pain!

UNDERTAKER *(tenor)*:
here's Missus Brown, here's Missus Brown
a goldtooth diadem planted in her crown
and her net bag and her buckled shoes
hatpin and zircon

MISSUS BROWN *(soprano, can sing if she finds a tune to fit)*:
I'll be lying in the ground with my gold teeth
I'll be lying in the ground with my treasure buried round
when I'm rotting in the grave
then they'll say: now she'll behave
I'll be lying in the ground with my old gold teeth

UNDERTAKER:
hey Missus Brown, hey Missus Brown
is your old man Bluey here in town?

MISSUS BROWN:
nah, love, he's doin a stretch

UMLAUT:
Madam, Madam, the King of Pain is here to serve you

MISSUS BROWN:
gimme a bottle, sweetie, I'll
rub it on my foundered feet

ALTO *(distantly)*:
come ride the

TENOR *(distantly)*:
come ride the
merrygoround

MISSUS BROWN:
quite a carnival
you're runnin here

ALTO *(still far away)*:
ferris wheel

TENOR *(likewise):*
  carousel

UMLAUT:
  one night only, Madam
  perhaps you'll want two

MISSUS BROWN:
  one for each foot, dearie?
  what do you think you can do me for?

UNDERTAKER:
  hey Missus, hey Missus Brown
  don't you think it's time you thought of death?

MISSUS BROWN:
  sure love, to be sure love
  I think of death each time I take a breath
  what're you sellin now?
  what've you got?
  when it was potato-peelers
  they got rusty
  when it was eggbeaters
  my cake sank
  are you tryin to sell me
  an annuity
  in case my old man Bluey gets shot?
  well he's only a common thief, dear
  and he's so damn common he never brought in
  a penny to spare
  why can't us poor women have a Thief Relief?
  it isn't hardly fair

UNDERTAKER:
  Missus Brown my love
  it's you I'm thinking of
  I'm selling caskets

MISSUS BROWN:
  hah

UNDERTAKER:
  complete with plot

MISSUS BROWN:
  hoo

UNDERTAKER:
  just behave, missus
  and you'll save, missus
  put a dollar in the pot

MISSUS BROWN:
  a dollar down and nowhere to go

UNDERTAKER:
  and once you die
  you'll rise on high
  swing with the angels
  up in the sky

MISSUS BROWN:
  I'm lying in the ground with my gold teeth

UNDERTAKER:
  and be the envy
  of the Ladies Auxiliary

  I'll undertake to undertake to take you under sweetly
  I'll send you under six feet down
  both neatly and completely
  while the twenty-third psalm
  keeps the mourners calm
  with a min-i-mum of pain
  I'll write a guarantee
  in a hand so free
  that you'll never come up again

MISSUS BROWN:
  ah, you're gonna preserve me
  like old king Tut

UNDERTAKER:
    alas, an undertaker's lot
    is definitely not
    an utterly happy one
    no matter how he tries to stop the rot
    it's a thing that can't be done
    a mahogany box and a copper case
    give you only style and dash
    and I've got to admit
    he's doing it
    for a max-i-mum of cash

MISSUS BROWN:
    what happens to the undertaker
    when he dies?

UNDERTAKER:
                 he's taken over
    by another undertaker
    who shunts him down below the clover

MISSUS BROWN:
    I see! I see!
    you don't have to tell me more
    it ain't me you're waitin for, babe
    it ain't me you're waitin for

THE COMPANY *(singing)*:
    what shall we do with your body, missus
    where shall we hide your corpus, missus
    where shall we have your carcass, missus
    ear-ly in the morning?

MISSUS BROWN *(singing)*:
    heat it and serve it on paper dishes
    carve it up into bait for fishes
    yes, carve it into bait for fishes
    ear-ly in the morning

UNDERTAKER:
> nah, that wouldn't be proper, lady
> that sure wouldn't be proper, lady
> somebody'd think it was awful shady
> ear-ly in the morning

MISSUS BROWN *(singing)*:
> drop it in the well and make three wishes
> drop it in the well and make three wishes
> just be sure you don't act suspicious
> ear-ly in the morning

UMLAUT:
> please, that would cause pollution, Madam
> horrifying pollution, Madam
> hardly the best solution, Madam
> ear-ly in the morning

MISSUS BROWN *(singing)*:
> chop it up into fertilizer
> that way no one will be the wiser
> chop it up into fertilizer
> ear-ly in the morning

THE COMPANY *(singing)*:
> heave ho and up she rises
> into the flowers and leaves she rises
> maple and oak and pine she rises
> into God's green morning!

UNDERTAKER:
> goodbye, so long Missus Brown
> hope your old man Bluey's out soon

MISSUS BROWN:
> no hurry, love, there ain't no hurry
> I'll be lying in the ground
> with my treasure buried round
> I'll be lying...

(Missus Brown fades out)

UMLAUT:
   that's one you didn't get
   that's one you lost, my boy

UNDERTAKER:
   my trade may flourish like the green bay tree
   but it's no joy to wash the dead
   don't jeer at me
   I never said
   it was a joke or joy
   in my house flowers never live
   or children grow
   death's angel is my cousin but I never said
   he was my favourite relative

   and I'll get her yet
   her kind always wants to die respectable

SOPRANO *(far away)*:
   merrygoround, carousel

ALTO *(faintly)*:
   fishpond and ferriswheel

UMLAUT:
   the race is not to Swift's no matter how
   they pull the bull by the horn or slice the cow
   for the fish in the net and the bird in the snare
   can smother in the water and choke in the air
   NOT A THROUGH STREET/NO THOROUGHFARE

   but you can push back Death
   shake your fist in his face
   catch an extra breath
   stay abreast of the race
   get value for every second you gain
   with Doctor Umlaut's King of Pain!

(distant voices of barkers)

ALTO:
　try your luck, a quarter

SOPRANO:
　try your skill, a quarter

TENOR:
　take a shot, a quarter

ALTO:
　shoot to kill, thirty-five cents

UMLAUT:
　soldier, here's a bargain for you
　soldier, got a minute or two
　soldier?

SOLDIER *(his part is always taken by the two male voices speaking in
　unison except where indicated)*:
　clear glass bottle?

UMLAUT:
　yes!

SOLDIER:
　no cheap plastic?

UMLAUT:
　yes!

SOLDIER:
　price one dollar
　plus five cents tax?

UMLAUT:
　yes, yes!

SOLDIER:
　why not? I've drunk everything else

UNDERTAKER:
　soldier, you want a nice cheap
　convenient resting place
　a real bargain?

SOLDIER:
> there'll always be a place for me to die, man
> and somebody to build a tomb for me where I'm not

GIRL *(her part is spoken by the two women in unison)*:
> soldier

SOLDIER:
> yes

GIRL:
> got a minute?

SOLDIER:
> yes

GIRL:
> planning to do anything in it?

SOLDIER:
> got a suggestion?

GIRL:
> yes!
> soldier, will you come to me, come
> with your musket fife and drum da-da-dum

SOLDIER:
> I've been I've been wherever there is to be

GIRL:
> and you've seen whatever there is to see?

SOLDIER:
> right left right:
>
> I've shaken a spear with Caesar
> shoved the elephants over the Alps
> been shot in the eye with a crossbow
> nailed to a crucifix (two sticks)
>
> strung from a yardarm
> hung from a tree

GIRL:
> for what? for what?

SOLDIER:
> for raping and stealing and various other
> kinds of larceny
> had my skull split with a pike
> stuck one or two heads on a spike
> been slit up the belly and watched my tripes
> sliding like hot blue snakes

GIRL:
> it takes a lot of guts to be a soldier

SOLDIER:
> say it again you can say it again with the
> mud and the blood you can say it again
> I've fought with a Maxim and a Martini
> fought with a Bofors and a Bren
> fought with an axe and an assegai
> everything went and so did I
> when I was called

> most of the time

(here the voices break step and the baritone comes in with "when" as the tenor says "good")

TENOR:
> when it went
> > good

BARITONE: when it went good

(both:)   when I felt good
> I went for the whores like a soldier should

> and when I felt wild I might feed a child
> or cradle the head of a wounded man

and I hold on to life as hard as I can

GIRL:
if you want life, soldier
come on, come on
take it while there's time

WHORE *(alto)*:
ten and three

UMLAUT:
who's this? who's she?

WHORE:
ten and three

UNDERTAKER:
coming down the midway

WHORE:
my time is free

UNDERTAKER:
down the oldest way in the world
in a dress with sleeves
feathered at the edge
with a purposeful walk in a purple dress with

WHORE:
ten and three

UNDERTAKER:
sleeves feathered at the edge
hey miss, hey miss, have you time for me?

WHORE:
you? go on home to your wife

UMLAUT:
are you interested in a balm to sustain you
throughout the ills and the evils that pain you?

WHORE *(ultra-Brecht)*:
 I ain't buyin. I'm sellin.
 I'm ten and three
 I'm ten and three
 at ten and three my time is free

 three for the pillow and ten for the spread
 and none for the shadow that falls on the bed

 got your money? got your money?
 put your money where your mouth is
 never mind
 old Vice Squad flat in the feet flat in the head
 is giving me the eye: beg pardon sir
 oh beg pardon sir, do you have the time?
 yes miss oh yes miss it's ten-seventeen

 a-young-miss-like-you shouldn't be
 out-in-a-place-like-this
 oh thank you sir thank you sir
 I'm-going-home-right-now
 yes sir thank you sir go spit in your mother's beer

 as a girl who was fair I was called
 by the young who were hairy the old who were bald
 they made me their toy
 and I gave them all joy
 and a dose of the syph to each sweet mother's boy

 now I'm old and tough
 and my life's been rough
 and if I was smart I'd say that was enough

 but I walk my beat
 in the hollow street
 my shoes are too tight and I'm scared of the night
 but my time is free
 at ten and three
 my time is free
 my time is free

BROOM-GIRL *(soprano, coming in from a distance):*
  who'll buy my brooms?

WHORE *(growing fainter):*
  my time is free

BROOM-GIRL:
  who'll buy my brooms?

WHORE *(fading):*
  ten and three

BROOM-GIRL:
  tenpenny brooms
  pigeon-wing feather-dusters
  my brooms are not ragged
  but well-cut and round

UNDERTAKER:
  cherry-ripe too, miss?
  your lips are like cherries

BROOM-GIRL:
  my tenpenny brooms
  are very well bound

UNDERTAKER:
  if you were selling branches of cherries I'd buy them

BROOM-GIRL:
  buy my brooms
  to sweep your rooms
  chopcherry chopcherry jigajig

UMLAUT:
  Miss, sweet Miss, you seem to be ailing
  your cheek is so pale and your eyes are so brimming
  you seem to be
  a lass with a lackaday

BROOM-GIRL *(sweet but crisp):*
  what can I say?
  what else can I say?
  it's the usual story I tell
  how I loved him not wisely but too bloody well
  he filled up my belly

and left me for Nelly
and I hope it's God's truth that I'll meet him in hell

UNDERTAKER:
  what, in hell?

BROOM-GIRL:
  yes, in hell

UMLAUT:
  surely not in hell

BROOM-GIRL:
  hot crackling cinder-black and shrivelling
  I've got brooms to sell and I'll see you in hell
  John, for your
  chopcherry chopcherry jigajig

UNDERTAKER:
  miss, I pity him

BROOM-GIRL:
  buy my brooms, pity me
(gently now)
  did you show me pity, John?
  never, John, no

  will you lie with me on the bed
  against my body rest your head
  to feel the baby move within
  and swear such love could be no sin?

  no John, oh no, John
  oh no John, no, John, no

  in that cold room so crabbed and mean
  no broom will ever sweep it clean
  I lie and sweat and curse the time
  I must go clothed in blood and slime
  in that place where the basins freeze
  to scream the child between my knees
  will you be there, to touch my hair
  to kiss my bitten lips and swear
  this is the crown of love? not you, John
  never, John, not you

that's liniment you're selling, isn't it?
will that rub away a five-month belly?

UMLAUT:
liniment has its limits

UNDERTAKER:
so sweet a girl, so fresh and creamy

BROOM-GIRL:
yes, I'd look good in one of your coffins, wouldn't I?
threepenny feather-dusters, who'll buy, who'll buy?

WHORE *(faintly):*
I'm ten and three

BROOM-GIRL *(fading):*
tenpenny brooms, tenpenny brooms

WHORE *(very faint):*
my time is free

CLOCKSELLER *(tenor):*
who said time?
who said time?
who said time?
did I hear time?

UMLAUT:
I believe something of the sort was mentioned

UNDERTAKER:
go away, I'm tired of everything tonight

UMLAUT:
the ladies are snubbing him

UNDERTAKER:
everybody's selling
nobody's buying
business is a corpse
and I can't even bury it

UMLAUT:
  then you need Doctor Umlaut's King of Pain!

CLOCKSELLER:
  and you need time time time and again gain gain
  what I'm selling you is Time!

UNDERTAKER:
  another salesman

CLOCKSELLER:
  I sell Time
  in time pieces
  in mortgages deeds rents and leases
  in sundials sandglasses
  candles and clepsydras
  I sell mean time moon time
  star time noon time
  pendulums stopwatches
  Nuremberg eggs!

  and my time's
  going cheap going cheap
  and I get it get it get it
  at the source:
  there's a little old Timetaker in Geneva
  in a cellar with a trapdoor and a deep steep step
  and with his ratchets and his sprockets
  and his springes and his springs
  he begs borrows steals and bargains pieces of time
  with demons, with angels, with popes and with kings
  he catches tick in ratchets tock
  in sprockets tick and springs tock
  those demons tick those angels tock those popes
  and those kings

  and
  he
  brings
  them
  to
  me!

and I pay for them

I pay for them
with my heart's drip blood drop
bright red heart's blood
heart's tick blood tock

and
I
bring
them
to
you!

there's a Rolex Westclox Timex to wear when you love
there's an Accutron Omega Waltham to wear when you die
and when you get to the Pearly Gate
you can tell Saint Peter he's running late
the race is won under the sun under the sky!

I sell Time Time Time I sell Time on the line
and the Alpha and Omega shall be mine mine mine!

UMLAUT:
   time, gentlemen, time
   time to go
   time to pack up the show

CLOCKSELLER:
   sometimes time comes too close to me
   talk to me, talk to me
   say it isn't so
   my heartclock mocks me
   and my breath goes where the winds go
   don't make me go

ALTO:
   the dawn is coming

SOPRANO:
   cockadoodle, cockadoodle-doo

CLOCKSELLER:
  cuckoo!

ALTO:
  cocorico, cucaricaru

CLOCKSELLER:
  don't make me go

THE COMPANY:
  the dawn is coming on its big fat feet
  pick up, pick up, pick up your step
  ditchdigger, steelwalker, time study man
  don't tread on a crack
  stiffen your back
  hold up your head

THE MEN:
  limber your hands
  pull down the stands

MISSUS BROWN:
  cheer up, love, you'll soon be dead

THE WOMEN:
  morning is coming with the voice of the bird
  the sound of the grinders, the crackling of thorns
  the nightwinds falter, the sun
  straddles squares on the hopscotch street

THE COMPANY:
  pick up, pick up, pick up your feet
  hold up your head

OLD WOMAN *(alto)*:
  I'm pickin up I'm pickin up
  what's left over
  bottles bags and old rags
  I can't lift up my head because my back's crooked
  my feet's a bunch of bones with corns on 'em
  and I'm damned if I care about morning or night

here's a glove to put with one I found last year
they don't make a pair but they make two
left or right?

UMLAUT:
Madam, I have a bargain for you
Madam, Madam, a bargain for you
here's my last bottle and it's going cheap

OLD WOMAN:
cheap? man, you can call it cheap
I was too proud to ask the world and what the world gave me
you could put it in your eye and it wouldn't make you cry
I know what's a bargain and I know what's cheap
and I don't need to buy from you

so you can pour away your drop of pain
pour away your drop of pain
pour out your whatchamacallit panacea
spill your goddam thingamajig pharmacopeia
throw away your top hat frock coat cane
you don't know how it is with me

UMLAUT:
I am Umlaut, Madam!
and you insult me, Madam!
you disparage, defame, reject, humiliate
and shame me, Madam!

for I am Doctor Umlaut the paragon!
Doctor Umlaut the automaton!
I am seated at the feet
of the Tetragrammaton!

OLD WOMAN:
man, man, those are fine words
like angels with trombones
like cherubim with swords

but will you take my hand? and
will you walk with me?
will you lead me to Beulah-land?

I am so lonely, man
I am so lonely, man
I am so lonely, lonely, lonely, man

I live in a room where the walls press in
upon my twisted bones, upon my shrivelled skin
I got as old and ugly as a body can
but you don't know how much uglier it is than sin
to be so lonely, lonely, man

CLOCKSELLER:
    don't make me go

BROOM-GIRL:
    will you be there, to touch my hair

UMLAUT:
    I come home at night and lay down my staff

OLD WOMAN *(softly)*:
    I am so lonely, man

UMLAUT:
    turn the radio on
    and hear the voices calling down the winds

    I heat up my supper left from yesterday
    smoke my cigar, drink my beer

    look in the mirror
    comb out my beard and count the grey

OLD WOMAN:
    I am so lonely, man

UMLAUT:
    when I take off my clothes I see that I am
    only a piece of the flesh that is known as a man
    but I reach for the light as well as I can
    towards the light as well as I can
    brothers and sisters, there's a time to cast away stones
    time to gather stones together
    to consider love and giving

not to talk about the weather in the sky

ALTO:
    brothers and sisters, let me testify
    that we turn and turn again
    to the pain of other days
    vanity of vanities
    sowing vineyards in the seas

TENOR:
    the fool holds his hands and eats his heart
    and hates the light
    and the wise all their lives
    turn their breasts towards the knives
    and their hands towards each
    other in the night

SOPRANO:
    and the warmth between their bodies blesses
    all the world of light
    the world of light

from the arc of my darkness
each one forms my
quadrant of light
for a moment alone
then finds a shadow of his own

MATT COHEN

Matt Cohen is probably best known as a novelist, beginning with Korsoniloff, *published in the House of Anansi's Spiderline Editions in 1969, and continuing with the Salem novels, set in the farm country of Eastern Ontario and published between 1974 and 1981. However, he has also had a parallel career as a writer and editor of short stories; and where the Salem novels might be described as regional, Matt Cohen is a writer of fiction and a reader of his contemporaries, whose literary interests and sources are both local and international. A number of his stories have been broadcast on* Anthology *in the past fifteen years, including "Sentimental Meetings", which is included in his most recent collection of stories,* Café Le Dog *(McClelland & Stewart, 1983).*

●

Sentimental Meetings

Planet and sky met in a long curved strip of light. Joseph Benares rubbed his eyes, straightened his neck, disengaged the elbow of his neighbour from the pocket it was trying to make between his ribs.

"*Bonjour, mesdames et messieurs . . .*"

The voice of the captain came through the overheated air in a broken cloud of static. When Joseph turned from the shining silver of the sea to look towards the front of the cabin, he saw the stewardess was already beginning to distribute trays of microwave-heated buns to the sleeping passengers.

At nine-thirty he was in a taxi wheeling crazily through the traffic on the Rue de Rivoli. His suitcase had been the first off the baggage belt. Good luck? A token of appreciation for flying Air Canada? "Everything is worse than it was," the taxi driver complained. But the sky was blue and Paris sparkled as if it had just jumped, freshly-made, out of the tourist magazines.

When he locked the door of his room behind him, Joseph felt a brief moment of panic, the familiar nightmare of hotels falling like a blanket over the brilliant day. His hands began to shake, as if some new, unwanted neighbour had jostled him. He lit a cigarette, sat down on the bed, and focussed on the wallpaper. A wild tropical garden of violent yellows and greens leapt humidly from the wall.

Hands still trembling, he unpacked his suitcase. "Travel light," Tomas had told him, then laughed, his old man's voice breaking free in a sudden burst of life. "That way you can bring home souvenirs." Ironed shirts, two ties, a pair of formal shoes yet to be broken in, grey slacks, a sweater. Beneath his shirts was an address book. Printed in gold leaf on the cover, courtesy of a client: JOSEPH BENARES, BA, MD. On the blank pages were written the names his grandfather had given him. "These are your family," Tomas had pronounced, reserving for this statement the solemn tone of voice in which he annually predicted his death. "They belong to you. You belong to them."

Joseph went into the bathroom to splash water on his face. Black *spic* hair, parted in the middle and falling straight to his collar; olive skin stretched tight over high cheekbones; hazel eyes rimmed with red and surrounded by an increasingly defined network of lines and wrinkles. He was suddenly reminded of his first trip to Europe, more than fifteen years ago: then the face had been slightly thinner, the hair longer, the eyes red with drinking instead of reading.

The garden on the wall had subsided to a mild hum. Joseph went downstairs, where he handed in his key, then walked through the crowded streets until he was at the Jardin des Tuileries. On the airplane he had been thinking about Christopher Columbus: not the voyage to the New World, the sudden shock of the future. He had been trying to imagine the savages Columbus had brought to display to Ferdinand and Isabella. What had the poor kidnapped victims made of the glittering Spanish court? According to the books they had failed to be impressed—in fact, they had reacted to the cradle of civilization by growing sick and dying.

Joseph stopped at the entrance of the Jeu de Paume. Inside were real paintings, paintings immortalized ten million times on posters pasted across the walls of North America.

"*Monsieur, s'il vous plaît*, please!" In front of him was an old woman, dressed like Raggedy Ann. Joseph reached into his pocket, the unfamiliar French coins thick between his fingers.

"A family friend" was how Tomas had described her. She was the niece of a second cousin once-removed, a connection that would have been entirely meaningless had not Joseph instantly seen that despite her official distance she was only a slightly foreign model of his own exact family.

She answered the door and waved him in. About fifty years old; spiky salt-and-pepper curls; a silk dress carelessly worn over a body that might once have been beautiful but was now retreating to the wiry Benares frame; hazel eyes that were duplicates of his own. As she was taking his coat she suddenly turned and grasped his shoulders, kissed him on both cheeks.

Still not a word, and as he followed her into the apartment Joseph suddenly wondered if she was a mute. "She lives alone," Tomas had said, but without adding whether she had once been married, or if her aloneness was simply a disease—the same disease, perhaps, that Joseph had: thirty-seven years old and unmarried, all the Benares genes and chromosomes begging to be reproduced. There were no pictures of husband or children on the walls, so Joseph assumed that the "family friend" had also failed to multiply. But because she was a woman and past the age, her position was definitive: her supply of eggs—about four hundred, according to the textbooks—had all dropped into oblivion.

"English!" she suddenly burst out.

"English," Joseph repeated.

"You speak English," she said, in English. But her accent was disturbing.

"Yes."

"Do you speak a little French?"

"A little."

"I speak French," she said, still in English, and Joseph realized that her accent had been borrowed from Greta Garbo. Her name was Hanna Santangel, but on the mailbox in the foyer it had been engraved Mme H. G. Santangel. Now Joseph felt like an awkward schoolboy faced with an exam he hadn't prepared for.

"*C'est un plaisir de*—" he began stiffly, but Hanna interrupted him before he could even pause to search for the right phrase, cut him off with a flow of English so voluble and sibilant that Joseph had no idea what she was saying. Then she was in his arms, weeping and sobbing and talking all at once. When she stepped back, reaching into her sleeve for a handkerchief, her face had been transformed from that of an elegant and impervious Parisian to that of a crying child.

"There were so *many* who were killed." She opened the drawer of the buffet which immediately spilled over with hundreds of photographs. Hanna grabbed them in handfuls, displaying them for a second then dropping them to the floor as she reached for more. "First Franco and then Hitler. Look." Joseph felt the tears streaming out of his own eyes; they had started without his noticing. And he was crying, not only in sympathy with this stranger's sudden outburst of emotion, not only out of sorrow for the other millions of strangers who had died, but for the whole jumbled parade of pictures, the universe forgotten, the cascades of family snapshots—carefully posed portraits, lovers holding hands or trying to look serious enough for a wedding; children crinkling their foreheads to make themselves look like bullfighters or movie stars—all of them with the Benares stamp, all of them in some strange way exactly alike, natives of the country of which Joseph had suddenly found himself a citizen.

It wasn't until late at night, when a bottle of wine had warmed them, then been followed, first by a pot of coffee to keep them awake, and then by cups of hot chocolate to help them keep cosy in the hours after midnight, that Hanna Santangel brought out her oldest treasure, the will of her great-great-great-grandmother, a woman who had been born in a Jewish ghetto in Kiev more than two hundred years ago.

The will had been written on parchment, and the parchment itself was yellowed like the skin of a very old man. It was written in Hebrew, which he had learned to read as a child. Hanna made him pronounce the words aloud, only translating as he finished each sentence.

"You are not much of a Jew," she laughed. "You don't even know your own language." But then, as he blushed: "I was only joking. When they come to round us up, I promise you will be included."

She had shown him everything. Her tears, the photographs, the scrap of parchment that had evaded two centuries of destruction. Now she gathered up the evidence and put it away in the buffet drawers. As she bustled about, restoring the room to its original order, Joseph had the sudden feeling that they were becoming strangers again.

She turned to him. Joseph stood up, knowing it was time to leave.

"You must be exhausted," Hanna said, "listening to my rantings. I can't let you go back to the hotel like this, in the middle of the night."

"It's nothing."

"I insist. You didn't come all the way across the ocean to stay in a hotel."

When Joseph woke up he could hear the shower from the room next to him. By the time he got to the kitchen, Hanna was there, her short hair wound into tiny damp curls.

"You slept well?"

"I dreamt about the will."

Hanna smiled. "The will is nice to have seen, but I would like to offer you something more, something that is real. If you can spare me a little of your holiday. . . ."

At the hotel, the clerk looked at Joseph with a knowing smile. "You found a good restaurant last night?"

"I found an old friend."

Joseph saw the clerk's face suddenly freeze, then move into a question mark. He realized that in his fatigue he had forgotten to speak French, had spoken Spanish instead.

"Excuse me," said the clerk, "I thought you were an American."

"As a matter of—"

"Breakfast will be sent right away to your room, *señor, milles excuses*."

In the bath Joseph looked down the surface of the steaming water to his protruding toes. "Feet tell the story," a landlady had once advised him.

On his right foot, his big toe was bent and misshapen. During an argument with his wife, his ex-wife, in fact, he had emphasized a certain point by kicking one of the heavy porcelain lamps her mother had provided as dowry towards the picture window in their living room. In the heat of his anger Joseph had wanted to drop-kick the lamp—or better, his wife—through the thermopane glass and onwards to a ten-storey journey to the sidewalk below. Instead, the joint of his toe had cracked on impact. Joseph, too furious to go to the hospital, had bandaged it himself. When he finally did leave Judith, he was still limping, hardly able to carry his suitcases to the elevator where Judith, her eyes suitably swollen, waved goodbye.

Out of the bath, Joseph dressed himself in the white suit he had bought for the journey. He was short, wide-shouldered, the desire of his stocky, ex-soccer-player's body to run to fat only partly warded off by frequent, boring sessions in the university swimming pool. Today his eyes were darker. My emeralds, Judith used to call them, when the motor between them was well and purring. Olive pits, she would say, when it wasn't.

Having slept since his return from Hanna's, Joseph found himself ferociously hungry. Walking the back streets from his hotel towards Montmartre, he stopped beside a huge mounded display of fresh shellfish. He leaned over a basket of raw oysters until he was enveloped in their briny smell. Moments later he was inside the restaurant, a bottle of sparkling white wine and a platter of clams in front of him.

"Joseph Benares!"

Joseph's head jerked up. The voice, the face, gradually filled his mind like an unwanted image slowly coming into focus during a bad film.

"Mind if I sit down? Who would have thought to see a white man in this country?"

Norton Meredith's voice slipped out like an unnecessary subtitle. First Joseph had found himself remembering long-buried scenes with Judith; now here was one of the original supporting cast: Norton Meredith, best man at the wedding, court witness at its legal dissolution.

"Excuse me for not shaking hands," Joseph said. "They're covered with clam juice."

"For God's sake, Joseph, how *are* you? You look *great*."

"Thanks, Norton."

"I stopped drinking years ago, but I admire those who keep it up, despite everything. Go ahead, don't mind me."

Norton Meredith, Joseph slowly realized as the close-up of his face receded and his whole body became visible, had changed more than his drinking habits. He was wearing a black leather jacket, gleaming and supple, and about his neck was wound a white silk scarf. His hair, silver, was down to his shoulders, and when he shook his head with delight Joseph could see that he had gold earrings.

"I *moved* here. Got right out of the rat race. Never *felt* so good. Set up a practice treating homesick tourists. I *love* it here. What's *Judith* doing?"

"We're divorced."

"I *know* that. But don't you keep in touch? Even today, it's more unusual to get divorced than to get married." Norton paused, then smiled, a gleaming display of ivory and gold.

"You look great," Joseph said. "You really do."

"I thought you'd *never* notice. I came out."

"That's wonderful."

"Not out of the *closet*, you fool, I'm not a faggot. I mean that I came out of my shell. I'm *myself* now, none of the old defences."

"Congratulations."

"You old cynic. Come to dinner tonight, meet my *maîtresse*, nothing special, she has lots of friends. Someone for you."

"I promised my aunt."

"Forget your aunt. Or bring her. You know, Joseph, since coming to Paris the old *fires* have heated up again. I can't get enough."

"That's wonderful."

"If you can't come tonight, how about tomorrow? I have a card, here—"

"Norton, I'd love to visit you. But I'm leaving Paris tomorrow. Maybe when I get back."

"Where are you going?"

"Spain, with my aunt, I promised—"

"Keep your promises," Norton Meredith said. "And don't worry about me. I'm in a clear spot now, I can come with you. Really, it's no problem." He stood up. "I'll meet you at the airport and, look Joseph, let's be straight. Do you still hold it against me? One night, she wanted comfort. That was all. You know what master Freud says, Joseph. Sometimes a cigar is just a cigar."

Both of the guards were elderly and fleshy, dressed in black uniforms that must have fit better when their muscles were younger. "*Guardia Civil*," Hanna spat out as they walked towards the synagogue. *Synagoga del Transito* it was listed in the guidebook, the most beautiful synagogue in Spain and the entire world.

The guards stood in front of the door, smoking and talking, and even as he mounted the steps Joseph could see that the ticket window was closed.

"The synagogue is not available today."

The guidebook explained that the synagogue had been built by Samuel Halevi during the fourteenth century. Earlier in the day they had gone to Halevi's palace, now a national monument. It was, the guidebook pointed out, entirely reconstructed on historical principles. Unlike his palace, Halevi had survived neither intact nor reconstructed. An over-zealous investigator had tortured him to death while trying to discover the hiding place of his supposedly fabulous riches.

"We would like to see inside the synagogue," Hanna said slowly, as if talking to an idiot.

"It is occupied today," replied the guard, turning away.

Hanna pushed past him into the lobby. Joseph followed. To the right was a door which had a sign proclaiming it a library of ancient Hebrew books and documents. It, too, was closed.

A van pulled up outside the synagogue, its muffler-less motor roaring in the heat. The doors opened, television cameras began to emerge.

"Look," Hanna said to Joseph, who was already looking.

The director was talking to the guards, all smiles, a letter was being shown. Joseph heard the guard say that yes, he had a difficult job. It was better to work guarding one of the great Cathedrals, the truly magnificent churches whose visitors understood the duties—

"They're German!" Hanna suddenly exclaimed.

She was right. The film crew were talking German among themselves as they dragged their cameras up the steps and into the doors of the synagogue which were now flung open.

"They're getting in," Hanna complained to the guard. "Why can't we? This is my nephew, a very important man, a doctor. He is all the way from America and I have brought him here, from Paris, to see the roots of his people."

"The synagogue is closed," the guard repeated. But now Norton Meredith had appeared from around the corner and was engaged in violent conversation with the film director. Taking his white scarf from his neck and waving it as he spoke, one hand on the director's shoulder, Norton led him towards the guard.

"These people are my guests," the director now said. "There has been a misunderstanding." He was blond, a Teutonic Viking. He stepped between Joseph and Hanna, put his arms around them and ushered them inside the synagogue. "Bureaucrats," he said, switching to English now that they were inside. "They're the same in every country."

Within a few minutes floodlamps had been set up, the entire synagogue staked out by the crew. There were no prayer benches, no ark for the scrolls, no altar. The building was as bare as an empty warehouse. Five hundred years ago the synagogue had been turned into a church; more recently it had been restored as a tourist attraction.

"...a documentary on religious freedom," the director was explaining to Hanna. "I want to show that people are finally, after so much bloodshed, free to follow the god of their choice."

"There is only one God," Hanna muttered. "And people don't choose Him, He chooses them."

"That is your opinion," the director said with a smile. The sounds of camera motors filled the room; electric whirrings that buzzed about like gigantic moths, the floodlights trailing their course.

"We wanted to film people praying," the director said. "Heart to heart is the most effective, one person to another."

"No one prays here."

"So I was told. I tried to find a Rabbi in Toledo, but he was unavailable."

"You should have been here six hundred years ago. There were dozens of Rabbis then."

The director smiled. "The Jewish community has become very secretive. Believe me, I understand these things. During the war—"

"You are a very intelligent man."

"Between intelligent people it is possible to discuss these things, to put the past behind us."

They were staying in a hotel that had been converted from the palace of a Cardinal. The doors of the hotel were reinforced with steel flanges, the windows barred. "Look at these," Hanna said to Norton, pointing to the door and the bars, "these show how much the people loved their Cardinals."

"Love must go both ways," Norton replied. "Believe me, I know."

There was a new, honeyed note in Norton's voice, a professional tone that he must have learned to use on his homesick tourists, and as Joseph winced he saw Hanna draw back as if she had been buzzed by an unpleasant insect.

In his room, Joseph splashed water on his face and hands, looked up at his face in the mirror. "You can't pass a mirror without staring at it, " Judith had once said angrily when, in the middle of a fight, he had been frozen by the expression of his own contorted anger in the living-room mirror.

That was the last fight, the one that had ended with him packing his books and clothes into one of Tomas's gigantic leather travelling bags. Perhaps that was the very night Norton had been summoned for help. Perhaps that was even the night when Norton, until then an awkward psychiatric resident with the breaking voice of an adolescent, had learned to speak in smooth and reassuring words.

But no matter how hard he tried, Joseph was never able to remember Judith's face. Even now, missing her for the first time in years, he was unable to summon more than her green-brown eyes and the peculiarly tufted hairs that grew at the centre of her eyebrows.

At the actual moment of the divorce, long after the final separation, Joseph had looked across the room at Judith, wondering if some unexpected and cosmic reconciliation might still take place. While other couples parted, she had come to sit beside him, leaning her shoulder into his chest for comfort the way she used to, bending her mouth to his so that he would hear her whispers.

Matt Cohen

"How have you been? You look good. Norton tells me you gave a wonderful lecture last month." And he had whispered back, whispers as close as kisses, saying that he was fine, that Norton was still an ass-hole, that she was looking more beautiful than ever, that she must have gone south to get such a winter tan.

Afterwards they had gone to the courthouse coffeeshop, the three of them. When Norton excused himself Judith had leaned over to Joseph and said that she still loved him: maybe they should go back to her place—one last time to make the ending happy.

Now Norton had made another tactical disappearance, and Joseph was alone in the hotel dining-room with Hanna. After coming back from the synagogue she had been so angry that lunch, served in the immaculately white dining-room, had made her violently ill. But she had returned to the table and the wine. "A friend of the family, a real guardian angel." Joseph again remembered Tomas's description. "A saint."

"Look at them," Hanna gestured, pointing to the bus-loads of tourists who were enjoying their meals without getting sick. "Even these pigs do not want to put their past behind them."

"You're feeling angry," Joseph said soothingly, as if Hanna was a patient to be babied. "Try to let yourself relax."

"Relax!" Hanna sputtered. But she ordered a cigar from the waiter, who delivered it to her without comment. Soon the odour of cigar smoke filled the room and, calmed, Hanna ordered a bottle of Calvados to be brought to their table.

By four o'clock the dining-room was almost empty. So was the bottle. Hanna was on her fourth cigar and had already explained to Joseph how the Castilian kings, beginning with the massacre of the Jews in Toledo in 1391, had taken over one hundred years to climax their drive to rid Spain of its Muslim rulers. "In 1492, the reconquest was finished. Ferdinand and Isabella were on the throne and for the first time in eight hundred years Spain was ruled by Spaniards—and Christians. To celebrate they expelled all the remaining Jews and sent Columbus off to discover the New World."

"What about the Inquisition?"

Hanna's voice dropped to a tone so low and bitter Joseph could barely hear her words. "I don't have to tell you what *that* was like. To amuse the population the priests organized gigantic acts of faith —in which Jews were tied to the stake and burned. These often took place in the sites of the old Roman circus, where the Romans

201

tortured the Christians. And yet, if you speak to a medieval scholar about such things, he will tell you that the medieval mind knew nothing of the concept of irony."

In the far corner of the room a new party was being seated: it was the television director and his crew. Beside the director, and talking loudly in a strange mixture of German and English, was Norton Meredith. In the course of the afternoon he had changed into a white silk suit. With his silvery hair and bright scarlet cravat he looked like an over-priced gigolo.

Before Joseph could deflect her attention, Hanna had spotted them. "Pigs," she said, in a voice that carried across the empty room. The director stood and bowed to her. On Hanna's pale cheeks now appeared two round red discs, like make-up carelessly applied by her anger and the Calvados.

"I met those types during the war. Do you have them at home?"

Joseph shook his head. Home? He could hardly remember it. Even the airplane trip from Toronto to Paris was a dream fast receding. The waiter was arriving with a bottle of champagne on a tray. Two glasses. "Compliments of an admirer," he said to Hanna. Hanna leaned across the table and kissed Joseph on the lips. She tasted like cigars, but her lips were soft and sweet just the same.

"Cheers," Hanna said. "That was very kind of you."

"It wasn't—"

"Don't tell me. I don't want to know. Anyway, the fool ordered French champagne. Spanish is better."

Two glasses into the champagne, Joseph felt his head come miraculously clear. He ordered a package of cigarettes and a second bottle of champagne, this time Spanish. He also requested that a new box of cigars be brought to the table.

"No more champagne," Hanna directed, "without brandy to accompany it. Otherwise the bubbles make me dizzy."

Joseph discovered that it no longer mattered whether his eyes were open or shut. Either way he was presented with a roseate haze of which Hanna was the out-of-focus centre. The new champagne was brought, uncorked, consumed. As they drank, Hanna was telling him about her war experiences. Terrible nightmares. Moments of comfort. "Imagine that," she said over and over again, urging him to the full horror. But despite his best efforts he was unable even to remember what she had just described, let alone imagine it.

"Terrible."

"I've never met an American who could drink so much."

"I'm not an American. I'm Canadian."

"There's a difference," Hanna said, "but I keep forgetting what it is."

They were standing up, and suddenly Joseph realized that her compliment was deserved. He wasn't drunk at all. In fact the whole room pulsed with a brilliant clarity that was more real than ordinary reality, even more sober than ordinary sobriety. As he straightened his back and stretched, Joseph felt such a burst of well-being and confidence that he lent poor Hanna his arm. She stood on tiptoe and Joseph seemed to imagine that she was still talking to him. "Before Tomas left Spain he brought me from Madrid to Toledo for a week, to see a specialist for a rare disease I had contracted. My disease, a consuming desire to be drowned in the arms of Tomas Benares, went away soon enough. In the meantime he showed me the city of our ancestors." Before Joseph could even imagine his dwarfed and aged grandfather with this strange woman, Hanna started forward and Joseph, arm linked with hers, began to stride out of the dining-room.

"Good evening."

Joseph turned, sensing a vague half-wanted familiarity. Then Norton Meredith spoke again. Words of extraordinary brilliance began to form themselves in Joseph's mouth. Then he pitched face forward across the heavily laden table of the director.

"A nice dive." The director's voice was only inches from his ear. "Daring and full of spontaneity. Truly, my friend, today you are showing us the best side of America."

"Head first, too," Hanna added. "That showed a lot of style for someone who travels with only two shirts. Frankly, I admire the courage of such a gesture."

The cells of Joseph's mind felt suddenly invaded, and what had been so brilliantly clear was entirely fogged over. The director and Norton Meredith had lifted him into the air, carried him like a dead man to his hotel room, and slid him, clothes and all, down the cold porcelain of his bathtub. Then they left the room while Hanna removed his clothes and turned on the water. Now he was naked in the steaming bath, modestly covered by a thick layer of the rosy bubblebath Hanna had so thoughtfully provided.

"Are you sore?"

"Sore?" Joseph squeezed his eyes closed and sent an inquiring scout beneath the surface of the water. After a few moments it reported that sensation had completely disappeared from his bones and his muscles.

"You are feeling no pain," Joseph said.

"*I* am feeling no pain," Hanna corrected.

"Could I have a cigarette?"

Hanna wiped his face with a towel, put a cigarette between his lips, lit it for him.

Joseph felt his lips make contact with the filter, a sharp sensation as the smoke filled his lungs. As he exhaled he noticed that he was beginning to see again, though the room was still smudged. He put a hand to his glasses, lifted them off. One lens, the rose-coloured one, was covered with an uneven layer of tomato sauce. The other was curtained in what might have been coffee with double cream. He dipped his glasses in the water, drew them out again. Save for a slight mist, the bathroom snapped into focus. But Hanna's scarlet and the rosy happiness of her bubblebath survived intact.

Now the director and Norton Meredith came into the room. The director approached Hanna first, leaned over and kissed her neck. Hanna jerked back, but not too quickly.

"Don't mind me," the director said, "I'm off duty." He sat on the edge of the tub, brandy glass in hand. "Is this your first trip outside of America?"

"I'm not American, I'm—"

"He's a Jew," Hanna interrupted. "Jews are international."

"That's it," Norton exclaimed. "A man who travels discovers *himself*."

"Of course," agreed the director. He leaned over the tub, his muscular arm stretching across the water until his long white fingers came to rest on Joseph's naked chest. "Welcome home."

ACKNOWLEDGEMENTS

The Shining Houses, by Alice Munro, from *Dance of the Happy Shades* (McGraw-Hill Ryerson, 1968), copyright © by Alice Munro and reprinted by permission of the author.

Galapagos poems, by Al Purdy, from *Being Alive* (McClelland & Stewart, 1978), reprinted by permission of The Canadian Publishers McClelland & Stewart Ltd.

Nathan Cohen interview with Joyce Cary, reprinted by permission of Gloria Cohen.

A Private Place, by Joyce Marshall, from *73: New Canadian Stories* (Oberon Press, 1973), and *A Private Place* (Oberon Press, 1975), reprinted by permission of the author.

Four Jobs, by George Bowering, from *West Window: The Selected Poetry of George Bowering* (General Publishing, 1982), reprinted by permission of General Publishing Co. Ltd.

Natural History, by Audrey Thomas, from *Real Mothers* (Talonbooks, 1981), copyright © Audrey Thomas, reprinted by permission of the author.

We All Begin in a Little Magazine, by Norman Levine, from *Thin Ice* (Deneau, 1979), copyright © by Norman Levine, reprinted by permission of the author.

Conversation between Northrop Frye and Robert Fulford, reprinted by permission of the authors.

May Day Rounds: Renfrew County, by Joan Finnigan, from *Living Together* (Fiddlehead Books, 1976), reprinted by permission of the author.

Aga Dawn, by Bill Schermbrucker, from *Chameleon and Other Stories* © 1983, Talon Books Ltd.

Poems, by Margaret Atwood, from *Journals of Susanna Moodie* (Oxford University Press, 1970), reprinted by permission of Oxford University Press Canada.

Causation, by Helen Weinzweig, from *Small Wonders* (CBC Enterprises, 1982), reprinted by permission of CBC Enterprises.

The Night Manny Mota Tied the Record, by W. P. Kinsella, from *The Thrill of the Grass* (Penguin Books, 1984), copyright © W. P. Kinsella, reprinted by permission of Penguin Books Canada Ltd.

The T. E. Lawrence Poems, by Gwendolyn MacEwen, from *The T. E. Lawrence Poems* (Mosaic Press, 1982), reprinted by permission of Mosaic Press.

205